STO

FRIENDS
OF ACPL

W9-DBR-256

Walter Scheithauer

Hummingbirds

Translated by Gwynne Vevers

With 76 colour photographs by the author

598.899
Sch2h

Thomas Y. Crowell Company
Established 1834 · New York

First published in the United States of America in 1967

Originally published in West Germany under the title KOLIBRIS

Copyright © 1966 by
BLV Bayerischer Landwirtschaftsverlag GmbH

English translation copyright © 1967 by
Arthur Barker Ltd and Thomas Y. Crowell Company

All rights reserved. Except for use in a review, the reproduction or
utilisation of this work in any form or by any electronic, mechanical,
or other means, now known or hereafter invented, including photo-
copying and recording, and in any information storage and retrieval
system is forbidden without the written permission of the publisher.

Text printed in Great Britain
Illustrations printed in West Germany

L.C. Card 67-24400

Contents

Preface   9

1420366

Introduction   13

What they are and how they live   15

Names, origin, appearance   17

*A galaxy of names – Where they occur, where they migrate
to – Distribution of the individual species – The gentle art of
catching hummingbirds – High-performance aircraft with head and
heart – Secret fire*

The marvel of hummingbird flight   38

*Rockets and aerial acrobatics – Vertical take-off and parachute
jumpers – With tail forwards – Costly observation – Instant
braking – The best helicopter – Fish or bird? – Nose dive – How
they catch flies – Courtship flight – The bird drill – Landing
without breaking the eggs – Solution of the problem: double power
output – With stopwatch and stroboscope – Incredible endurance*

Energy, food and body temperature   65

*Energy foods and banquets – Refuelling in the air – Plants
visited by hummingbirds – Do hummingbirds sleep? – Icy cold and
far out to sea*

The breeding season   72

*Magnificent architects – Model husband or Don Juan – Two-
chick system*

Hummingbirds and man   87

In South America   93

Hummingbirds as lucky charms – Eucalyptus trees and honey-pots

In Europe   97

*Sensation over the first ever – Difficulties of overseas transport –
Settling down in a dressing-gown – Which species to keep –*

Aeronauts in showcases, indoor aviary and living-room –
Uniform temperature and fresh air – Home comforts without
eucalyptus trees – The pleasure of bathing

Feeding 119
Nectar or insects? – A mixed diet but how to do it? – Long-term
observations on record-breakers – Brown Inca as taster – 730 days
of experiment and the results

Behaviour 149
Knight without fear and blemish – Not sociable but needing
company – Curiosity greater than fear – Intelligence tests – A man
for a sleeping perch – More obstinate than an elephant – Can
hummingbirds be tamed? At home everywhere – Beatles among the
song-birds – Always active

How to photograph
hummingbirds in flight 161

First attempts 163
An Egyptologist in the rain-forest – Hummingbirds are not ducks

The technical equipment 166
Camera – Electronic flash – Light trap – Important accessories

Methods 170
By accident or design – Management combined with endless
patience – A hundred exposures for one good photograph

In praise of the creation 174

Index 175

Species illustrated

Acestrura mulsanti	90 124
Aglaiocercus kingi	73 89 138
Amazilia franciae	44
Amazilia iodura	74 121
Amazilia tzacatl	73 106
Anthracothorax nigricollis	41
Boissonneaua flavescens	74
Boissonneaua jardini	90 140
Calothorax lucifer	108
Chlorostilbon mellisugus	41 124
Chrysolampis mosquitus	25 28 41
Cinnyris venustus falkensteini	60
Coeligena torquata	57
Coeligena wilsoni	58 73 107 139
Colibri coruscans	59
Damophila julie	91 92 122 123
Ensifera ensifera	76
Eriocnemis luciani	26
Eutoxeres aquila	105
Florisuga mellivora	58 75
Heliangelus exortis	27
Heliodoxa rubinoides	42 137
Heliomaster longirostris	43
Heliothryx barroti	76
Hylocharis leucotis	27 124
Lesbia victoriae	42 76 108
Loddigesia mirabilis	87
Popelairia conversii	105
Popelairia popelairii	15
Selasphorus rufus	90

Preface

The first live hummingbird to arrive in Europe was a Sparkling Violet-ear (*Colibri coruscans*) which was exhibited in 1905 at the Zoological Gardens in Regent's Park, London. For fourteen days it created a sensation and the many visitors who saw it were filled with astonishment and wonder. Then it died. It had presented more problems to science than any other known bird. Practically nothing was understood about its care and management; the correct food was certainly not known. Under these circumstances it was not possible to keep this exceptionally beautiful bird alive.

Although this first importation of a hummingbird took place some sixty years ago and many fine consignments have since been brought to Europe, many problems concerning the life of hummingbirds still remain unsolved. Several superficial observations were exchanged, but these proved to be unreliable. These strange creatures are still surrounded by an aura of mystery.

Almost every day inquiries reach me from all parts of the world which show the magical charm that is exerted by these jewels of the bird world. I have written this book in an attempt to assemble all the answers to these questions insofar as this is possible in the present state of our knowledge.

My aim is to report on all the most important ornithological aspects but above all to produce a guide to the correct care of hummingbirds under temperate climatic conditions. I have drawn on my own experiences – including the results of basic study and observations which yielded fresh information – and also on the experiences of the European zoos, which helped by providing available information.

The well-being of these birds in captivity is dependent upon several factors but primarily on correct feeding; I therefore began by studying the opinions of both old and modern biologists on what was assumed to be the natural diet of these birds.

The opinions of the different authors varied greatly. One person maintained that hummingbirds lived mainly on insects, another

9

held that their principal food was the nectar from flowers. Since only one diet could be correct, the other proving inadequate or even fatal in the long run, I realised that my first job was to investigate this problem thoroughly. After three years of systematic experiments with a hundred hummingbirds, representing thirty different species, I believe that I have solved the problem of diet.

The most difficult task of all was to photograph hummingbirds on the wing. In plunging flight these tiny birds reach a speed of over sixty miles per hour. The frequency of their wing-beats is comparable to that recorded for insects. It may be as high as two hundred beats per second!

Naturally, it is possible to focus on smaller and even faster moving objects, for example bullets, but only when the direction in which they are travelling is known in advance. With hummingbirds, which constantly twist and turn at high speed, this is not possible. By constant observation one can acquire a certain amount of empathy, but even a single photograph may be the result of long hours, or days, of patient waiting, watching and concentrated work.

Attempts at using expensive commercially available camera equipment did not give satisfactory results. One has to set up specially constructed electrical and photographic apparatus of the greatest sensitivity and precision; this equipment is neither standard nor readily available for delivery direct from industry.

Even with the best equipment and an automatic lighting cabinet, one still has to rely on chance, and I often had to take up to two hundred exposures of a single hummingbird before I succeeded in getting it in a characteristic pose. In all I took more than ten thousand colour transparencies.

At first I tried to photograph each hummingbird together with the flower at which it typically feeds. This proved a hopeless undertaking. First, there was the long period of waiting for delivery of the bird, which was often in a weak and bedraggled state when it arrived. Then more months went by while I brought it into a condition suitable for photography. By this time the flower appropriate to the particular bird was no longer available from any source. If the plants happened to be in flower in a greenhouse then I lacked the bird. If by chance both were available, the flower withered before I got a usable photograph. Through sheer necessity

I was sometimes forced to lower my sights and accept far less than perfection.

The pictures in this book, together with the data, are such as might be obtained in a zoo or by a private aviculturist in Europe or North America.

In spite of the great expense, the unspeakable difficulties and set-backs, my 'flying jewels' gave me considerable pleasure and I was able to take all the incidental problems in my stride.

Their intrinsic beauty would stir the heart of any man or woman, more even than flowers and jewels. Looking after these beautiful birds and having them constantly under observation presented me with a glittering kaleidoscope which could not have been more colourful and enchanting.

Introduction

When I collected my first hummingbird at Munich airport I never thought that these small bundles of vibrating iridescence would provide me with problems of such magnitude. Looking after a hundred of them, initiating feeding experiments and making physiological observations, studying their behaviour and the literature – not to mention taking over ten thousand photographic exposures – all this entailed a mosaic of ornithology, dietetics, physics, chemistry, medicine and pharmacology. The problems became so complex that at one time I came very near to abandoning the whole project.

In the end it was Dr H. G. Klös, Director of the Berlin Zoo, who encouraged me to complete this book for those who want information on how to look after hummingbirds.

I would like to express my grateful thanks to the numerous scientists, firms and institutions who generously offered me their help. Although they were all overburdened with work, the word *hummingbird* acted like a charm and evoked assistance and advice from every quarter.

Nutrition I am indebted to Dr Müller, Director of the distinguished research department of the firm of Milupa-Pauly, Friedrichsdorf, for fifteen years of co-operation which was indispensable in establishing a systematic basis for the feeding experiments.

Ornithology Information was most willingly given to me by the directors or ornithologists of many institutions and zoos, in particular: Dr Brotzler, Stuttgart Zoo; Dr Encke, Krefeld Zoo; Dr Faust, Frankfurt Zoo; Dr Klös, Berlin Zoo; Professor König, Institute for Behaviour Research, Vienna; Dr Müller, Wuppertal Zoo; Dr Nicolai, Max Planck Institute for Behaviour Research, Seewiesen; Dr Poulsen, Copenhagen Zoo; Dr Steinbacher, Senckenberg Research Institute; Dr Wackernagel, Basel Zoo.

13

Identification of the birds Dr Diesselhorst very kindly made available the fine collection of birds and the valuable library of the Bavarian State Zoological Museum in Munich; he also placed at my disposal his extensive knowledge and practical experience.

Literature I received considerable assistance from the works of Crawford H. Greenewalt (*Hummingbirds*) and of A. Martin and A. Musy (*La Vie des Colibris*), which deal with the life of these birds in the wild, and also from other works in the library of the Bavarian State Museum.

Chemistry To Dr Hesse and Mr Lafrenz of the Technical College in Munich I am indebted for their ready co-operation and for their work in analyses that were often difficult and time-consuming.

Veterinary medicine Dr Geier of the Munich University Animal Clinic generously carried out a successful series of complicated investigations.

Camera The Linhof Camera Factory in Munich put at my disposal their very fine precision camera, the Linhof Teknika, for the photographic work.

Electrical technique My special thanks are due to Mr Edgar Mönch of Munich who allowed me, for months at a time, to use his equipment, specially constructed by him for taking fast-moving objects.

For stroboscope photographs I am indebted to the Grundig Factory in Fürth. The visual stroboscopy was carried out with a stroboscope of the firm AEG in Nürnberg.

The main performers The stars of this undertaking, the hummingbirds, gave a superb performance. They must forgive me if ever I misunderstood or misrepresented them. Limitations of the human mind and senses may have proved inadequate for the task of fully understanding these marvels.

THE AUTHOR

What they are and how they live

*Of all animated beings, the
hummingbird is the most
elegant in form and
the most brilliant in colour.
Stones and metals
polished by art are not
comparable to this gem
of nature.*

BUFFON

Names, origin, appearance

A galaxy
of names One has only to read the names of hummingbirds to feel that one is
already familiar with their appearance. Their names are so de-
scriptive and picturesque that they reflect the colourful and lively
nature of the birds themselves. As well as featuring the bodily
characteristics of the birds, including their colour, shape and form,
the names sometimes refer also to a bit of the history of their
discovery. As one reads the names one automatically knows what a
hummingbird is.

The family name Trochilidae could not be more appropriate. It
has to be admitted, of course, that there may be many ornithologists
who do not fully understand this word, which comes from the
Greek and means a bird. A better family name could not have been
found for the hummingbirds for they are *the* birds, the birds *par
excellence*, the ultimate in birds. They have feathers and they fly,
closer to heaven than earth. They avoid all that is pedestrian, such as
running, hopping, climbing and jumping. Even their nourishment
– their food and drink – and their daily bath are taken in flight.
When not perching they remain on the wing. This, after all, is the
life of a bird, a trochilus.

There is also the fact, as our popular name for them suggests, that
one can hear them, for they make a humming noise. The French
name for them is *oiseaux-mouches*, birds like flies, and it is not
difficult to see why the French call them this. The Spanish and
Portuguese name for them is *pica flor*, flower picker, or more deli-
cately and even more appropriately, *beija flor*, flower kisser, which
gives us an insight into their life. In the zoos at Berlin, Frankfurt,
New York and elsewhere the houses for hummingbirds are known as
Jewel Rooms and their occupants as flying jewels.

Their names suggest various kinds of jewels:

Amethyst, Blue-chinned Sapphire, Ruby-and-topaz Hummingbird, Crimson Topaz, Golden Throat.

Audubon called them glittering fragments of the rainbow, and
colour upon colour shine out:

Coppery Emerald, Brown Inca, Green Thorntail, Blue-tailed Emerald, White-tailed Hermit, Rufous Hummingbird, Violet-ear.

Then there are enchanting shapes:

Trainbearer and Puff-leg, Sabrewing and Racket-tail, Spatule-tail, Thorntail and Frilled Coquette.

Size and form are also referred to:

Giant Hummingbird and Bee Hummingbird.

The bill, often an astonishing structure, is also responsible for many names:

Sword-billed and Tooth-billed hummingbirds, Lance-billed and Straight-billed hummingbirds.

Some names give information on the distribution and habits of the birds:

Cayenne Hermit, Woodstar, Andean Emerald and Guiana Sapphire.

Many hummingbirds bear the names of scientists or their friends and relations. In this way we have memorials to some famous ornithologists:

Boissonneaua jardini,

after the Frenchman Boissonneaua and the Scotsman Sir William Jardine whose colour-illustrated monograph on the hummingbirds appeared in 1833.

Gould's Jewel-front,

after the Englishman John Gould, who produced a masterpiece with his *Monograph of the Trochilidae* in 1861.

Acestrura mulsanti,

after the Frenchman Mulsant who, together with his countryman Verreaux, published in 1874 an illustrated scientific work of considerable repute.

Phaethornis longuemareus,

also named after a French scientist of the nineteenth century, Longuemare.

Coeligena wilsoni,

in honour of the early American ornithologist Alexander Wilson.

These are but a few. In addition to the British, French and Americans, there are Germans who have hummingbirds named after them, such as Hartert and Reichenbach. Hummingbirds have also been named after persons of high rank:

> Princess Helena, *Calypte anna* (after the Duchess Anna), *Eugenes fulgens* (after the Duke Eugen), The Queen's Lover, Baron Rothschild, Comte de Paris, Empress Eugenie.

Hummingbirds are certainly accepted in high society but as if this were not enough, they have also been associated with mythology and portents in the skies. Sometimes their names convey an impression of dazzling brilliance and sometimes they are shrouded in mystery.

There are fairies, nymphs, sylphs and a plethora of spirits associated with mountains, trees, water and air:

> Black-eared Fairy and Purple-crowned Fairy, Wood-nymph, Blue-throated Sylph, and Gould's Heavenly Sylph.

And, finally, those which reflect the splendour of the heavens:

> Shining Sunbeam, Sappho Comet, Andean Rainbow, Orange-throated Sun-angel, Amethyst Woodstar.

There is a bewildering multiplicity of special names given to hummingbirds – many of which are easily explained – but I could find no explanation for the Caribbean word *kolibri*, which is now used as a collective term for hummingbirds in many European and other languages. Even Dr Diesselhorst, the Curator of Birds at the Bavarian State Zoological Museum, could find no etymological reference. He said: 'What do the words *falcon*, *tit*, *thrush* and *pigeon* mean? Their origin lies so far back that no one can possibly tell.'

Where they occur, where they migrate to

Hummingbirds have always provided zoologists, ornithologists and ecologists with food for thought. They have not allowed themselves to be completely codified, catalogued and classified in dusty folios. Nor are they easy to keep or breed in captivity. I cannot help deriving a certain amount of pleasure from the fact that, so far, these attractive creatures have managed to elude the tidy minds of zealous scientists.

They have evolved in a great many different ways, filling an unoccupied ecological niche, and have maintained themselves for thousands of years. They have become highly specialised, their mode of existence being a much tougher proposition than faces most other kinds of birds. Unlike the ubiquitous sparrow, which breeds freely, they survive by reason of their finely adjusted specialisation and their capacity to adapt themselves.

19

With the exception of the truly polar regions they have succeeded in adapting themselves to every kind of climate: cold, heat, dryness and humidity; indeed they can even tolerate snow and short frosts. From South America, where the evidence suggests they originated, they have colonised the whole of the western hemisphere. They are as much at home in tropical rain-forests with orchids and other epiphytic plants as with the cacti of the desert belt of Mexico and California; they occur in the temperate as well as in the sub-tropical zones and even in those regions that have scarcely any vegetation, including the inhospitable paramo zone of the high Andes on the edge of snow and ice. The small *Selasphorus flammula* lives alone, where no other bird flies, in the harsh climate of the craters of the Central American volcanoes.

Even man does not seem to frighten them away. They visit flower gardens and orchards, they build nests on houses – and in them – and frequently visit artificial feeding places, showing no sign of alarm.

The hummingbirds have one hundred and twenty-three genera and over three hundred and twenty species distributed over the whole of America. Half of them live in Ecuador and northern equatorial Brazil. The greater the distance from the equator, either to the north or south, the smaller becomes the number of species; they are reduced to three species up in the north to the west of the Rocky Mountains and to one species in southernmost South America, at the tip of Chile and Argentina and on Tierra del Fuego.

In fact, in the Americas, one can see hummingbirds almost everywhere that flowers are in bloom.

Many follow their food flowers in vertical and horizontal directions over great changes in altitude and distance. They move up and down the mountains. Some are migratory, covering long distances.

The tiny Rufous Hummingbird, *Selasphorus rufus*, flies from Alaska along the west coast of Canada, the United States and Mexico, until it reaches its winter quarters in Central America. This flight, extending almost from the Arctic Circle to the Tropic of Cancer, represents a journey of about 2,200 miles.

Stellula calliope, the little North American species, known as the Calliope Hummingbird, fights against all vicissitudes of climate in the same way. *Archilochus colubris*, known as the Ruby-throated Hummingbird to North Americans, familiar even to New Yorkers,

21

is a dwarf of not more than four grams; it crosses the Gulf of Mexico, thus flying approximately five hundred miles over the open sea to the Yucatan Peninsula of Mexico. It not only covers an incredible distance in non-stop flight, it shows evidence of astonishing toughness and tenacity to life in its struggles against storms, cold and rain. Of course, on a migration such as this some must succumb, but the species goes on.

We do not know whether hummingbirds in former times succeeded in reaching the Bahamas and Antilles by the land route, before the Central American land masses sank into the sea. They may have. The astonishing flying ability of the little *Archilochus colubris*, however, suggests that later they also reached these islands by flying over the sea.

The story of the evolution and distribution of the hummingbirds presents science with a puzzle comparable with that of deciphering the Egyptian hieroglyphics. It appears at first glance to be impossible to unravel the many different horizontal and vertical cross migrations or to explain the multiplicity of forms.

For a long time, some female hummingbirds were regarded as separate species because they were completely different in appearance from the males. Other species have been regarded as lost or extinct, such as the beautiful *Augastes lumachellus* which was only re-discovered a few years ago by Dr Ruschi in Brazil. The same scientist has also made a new discovery, namely the subspecies *Colibri delphinae greenewalti*.

When, where and how hummingbirds arose is unknown. Fossils have not been found. We are left with conjecture and hypothesis. Comparative anatomy suggests that these birds have originated from swifts or from swift-like ancestors. But although there are swifts all over the world the wonderful offshoot of hummingbirds has only evolved in America. Yet the same environmental conditions are present in Africa, Asia, Australia and even in the Mediterranean region of Europe.

Nature and evolution develop in ways which are not governed by any set rules. Where processes are apparently governed by chance or mystery, it is not possible to find any one guiding principle.

Distribution of the individual species

Tropical rain-forest	*Amazilia tzacatl*	Mexico and Central America
	Calliphlox amethystina	Brazil
	Chlorostilbon aureoventris	South-east of South America
	Chrysolampis mosquitus	Eastern South America
	Clytolaema rubricauda	South-east of South America
	Heliothryx aurita	Tropical rain-forest east of the Andes
	Heliothryx barroti	Pacific coast of South America
	Hylocharis sapphirina	Brazil
	Lophornis magnifica	Brazil
	Phaethornis eurynome	South-east of South America
	Phaethornis yaruqui	Western Colombia, Ecuador
	Thalurania furcata	Colombia, Venezuela
	Topaza pella	Amazon basin
Tropical dry regions	*Arphantocroa*	High plateau, Atlantic coast of Brazil
	Augastes	High plateau, Atlantic coast of Brazil
	Calypte anna	Hot regions of California
	Calypte costae	Deserts of California
	Clytolaema	High plateau, Atlantic coast of Brazil
	Heliaction cornuta	High plateau, Atlantic coast of Brazil
	Heliomaster constantii	Cactus areas of western Mexico
	Heliomaster furcifer	Dry regions of Argentina
	Hylocharis xantusi	Hot dry areas of California
	Leucochloris	High plateau, Brazil
	Melanotrochilus	High plateau, Atlantic coast of Brazil
	Myrmia micrura	Dry coastal stretches, Ecuador and Peru
	Rhodopis vesper	Dry coastal stretches, Ecuador and Peru
	Ramphodon	High plateau, Atlantic coast of Brazil
	Sappho sparganura	Sunny regions of southern Bolivia and northern Argentina
Subtropical regions	*Abeillia abeillei*	Mexico, Central America
	Acestrura mulsanti	Humid rain-forest, Ecuador
	Aglaiocercus kingi	Rain-forest, Colombian Andes
	Archilochus colubris	North America east to Mississippi; in winter, subtropical regions of Andes
	Boissonneaua jardini	Low-lying areas of the Andes
	Calothorax lucifer	Mexico

23

	Campilopterus	Mexico, Central America
	Eulampis jugularis	Lesser Antilles
	Lesbia victoriae	Dry areas of Andes in Colombia and Ecuador
	Ocreatus underwoodi	Rain-forest, Venezuela and Colombia
	Orthorhynchus cristatus	Lesser Antilles
	Sephanoides sephanoides	Chile
Temperate zone	*Angleactis cupripennis*	Andes, Colombia and Peru
	Chalcostigma herrani	South Colombia, north Ecuador
	Coeligena wilsoni	Andes slopes, Colombia, Ecuador; Costa Rica
	Colibri coruscans	Heights 4,500 to 10,000 feet, according to flowers
	Eugenes fulgens	Mountains of Mexico
	Heliangelus clarissae	Andes
	Heliodoxa	Temperate Andes, Colombia and Peru
	Klais	Colombia, Peru
	Selasphorus platycercus	Mountains above 3,500 feet
	Selasphorus rufus	Migrant, Alaska to Central America
Cold zones	*Lamprolaima rhami*	Mountains of Mexico, high regions of Guatemala
	Loddigesia mirabilis	Up to heights of 15,000 feet
	Oreonympha	Bleak paramo zone of Andes
	Oreotrochilus estellae	Up to heights of 15,000 feet
	Oxypogon	Up to heights of 15,000 feet
	Panterpe insignis	Craters of highest Central American volcanoes
	Patagona gigas	Bleak zone of High Andes
	Selasphorus flammula	Craters of highest Central American volcanoes
	Selasphorus torridus	Craters of highest Central American volcanoes

The gentle art of catching hummingbirds — If one wants to measure and weigh a live hummingbird one has first to catch it. Dr Augusto Ruschi of Brazil does it like this: he takes a kind of fishing-rod about eighteen to twenty-four feet long, with a whip-like tip of fibre-glass smeared with a sticky substance, a kind

One of the most beautiful Brazilian species, the tiny Ruby-Topaz Hummingbird, *Chrysolampis mosquitus* ♂, a flying jewel of enchanting beauty. The wings vibrate so fast – about one hundred wing-beats per second – that not even an electronic flash of 1/5000 second will produce a completely sharp photograph. The energy source for this prodigious performance is the nectar from flowers.

aggy trousers are
pical of the Sapphire-
ented Puff-legs,
riocnemis luciani (Peru).
he feathering covers
e legs almost com-
letely. This specimen
as wild and aggressive
d in human terms
rtainly wore the
ousers.

Above: My 'experimental guinea-
pig' *Hylocharis leucotis* ♂ (Brazil)
which for four years tolerated
feeding experiments, technical
tests and other unreasonable
demands and yet remained radiant
and unruffled.

Below: *Heliangelus exortis*, from
Colombia, weighs only 2·5 grams
and has an iridescent violet patch
on the throat. It is investigating the
flowers of a *Euphorbia fulgens*.

Overleaf: A female Ruby-Topaz
Hummingbird, *Chrysolampis
mosquitus*, at a flower of *Dipladenia
rosea* (much enlarged).

of bird-lime made of thickened linseed oil. He creeps up to the nearest hummingbird with the rod and angles for it, that is, he advances the sticky tip slowly and carefully over the bird until the latter sticks to it. Simple!

It is only necessary to know where there is a perching hummingbird, but one must have a very delicate sense of touch, far more sensitive than that of an angler; finally one also needs luck and endurance, for the operation may take some hours, or perhaps two to ten days.

Alternatively you can do it like the South American Indians. Take a long blow-pipe, load it with a soft damp pellet of lime and shoot the hummingbird. The bird falls to the ground dazed, provided you have hit it in the right place; you can then pick it up, put it in your pocket and carry it home in triumph. This, however, is by no means as easy as it sounds.

It is somewhat simpler for the man who has his own hummingbirds in an aviary but even then it is not all that easy! He enters the aviary with a net in his hand. The birds are already familiar with the net and so an hour's entertainment awaits them. They seem to be waiting patiently for the game to start as they hang stationary in the air, apparently taking it all quite calmly. You then make a strike with the net, a kind of sweeping action which might catch a canary but certainly not a hummingbird.

It does not fly blindly in one direction like a budgerigar or a song bird which sooner or later lands straight in the net. It waits stationary in the air, close in front of your nose, and watches you; at the right moment it jinks slightly to one side and slips away to safety. It reacts like a fencer who anticipates his opponent's lunge and parries it right from the start. Assuming that I am in reasonable form, my reactions correspond to those of an average tennis-player, whereas a hummingbird reacts at least ten times as fast. Its warning interval is only one-fiftieth of a second.

For a short time I thought I had discovered a better catching method. I climbed into the illuminated aviary at night, approached a perching hummingbird – without a net of course, because I did not want to make myself ridiculous again – switched off the light and plucked the bird like a fruit from the tree. This worked well for three days, then they learnt the trick. As soon as the light went out, they were off like lightning and I was left whistling in the dark.

29

Copenhagen Zoo recommended shooting them with a jet of water but this method seemed to me unsporting and also too dangerous for the birds which have to be completely soaked before they fall to the ground. I therefore returned to the old and laborious method with the net. Once you have caught your hummingbird you measure it by holding the bill with the thumb and index finger of your right hand, and the body with your left hand, carefully laying the bird on the table alongside a ruler or actually on it. The bill must lie flat, with the neck a little extended.

Hummingbirds are the smallest birds in the world. The smallest of them all, *Mellisuga helenae*, the Bee Hummingbird, has a body length of six-tenths of an inch, plus a bill of six-tenths of an inch and a tail of just over an inch.

The smallest hummingbird illustrated in this book is *Popelairia conversii*, with a body length of about one inch, which is not as long as the top joint of my little finger. Its bill is six-tenths of an inch and its tail-feathers are three-quarters of an inch. Even medium-sized hummingbirds, the *Amazilias* for instance, are only about three and a half inches in total length, of which one and a half inches are bill and tail; this is smaller than the European wren which measures four to four and a half inches in length.

Some species of hummingbird have a long bill or a long tail and wing feathers – far exceeding the body length – thus giving the impression of being bigger than they really are. The Sword-billed Hummingbird, *Ensifera ensifera*, has a bill like a lance, four and three quarters inches long, with a body length of only three inches. The Black-throated Trainbearer, *Lesbia victoriae*, is only two inches long but its tail feathers extend almost six inches behind it. Many of my acquaintances who still do not know much about hummingbirds only need to hear something about the diminutive size of these birds to feel that they must see them. Women and girls are particularly drawn to young or small animals. Whereas a man looking at a family of elephants usually admires the powerful bull, it is always the woman who notices the young and, completely captivated, blurts out, 'Oh, do look at the baby, isn't it sweet'. Hummingbirds are just a little smaller and so people fall in love with them straight away.

One of the larger hummingbirds, *Patagona gigas*, the Giant Hummingbird of the Andes, is only the size of a swallow – about eight and a half inches. In this species the tail and bill also account for more

than half the total length. A lot of feathers and bill, but very little bird!

The fact that hummingbirds have survived for thousands of years is due not only to their adaptability but also, doubtless, to their diminutive size. In order to find out the relation between their size, weight and the daily intake of food, I kept records of their weights. I let them fly singly into a small glass cage in which there was a precision balance with one arm that served as a perch. In effect, they weighed themselves, a less disturbing experience for them than being laid out on a table to be measured. Their weights are listed below. For comparison: a canary weighed 21 grams on the balance.

Popelairia conversii	♀	2·2	*Lesbia victoriae*	♀	5·0
Selasphorus rufus	♀	2·0	*Lesbia victoriae*	♂	5·5
Chlorostilbon mellisugus	♂	2·5	*Aglaiocercus kingi*	♂ & ♀	6·0
Acestrura mulsanti	♀	2·5	*Phaethornis jopi*	♂	6·0
Calothorax lucifer	♀	2·5	*Heliomaster*		
Acestrura mulsanti	♀	3·0	*longirostris*	♂ & ♀	6·0
Chlorostilbon mellisugus	♂	3·0	*Anthracothorax*		
Damophila julie	♂ & ♀	3·0	*nigricollis*	♀	6·5
Hylocharis leucotis I	♂	3·0	*Boissonneaua jardini*	♂	7·0
Chrysolampis mosquitus	♂	3·5	*Boissonneaua flavescens*	♂	7·5
Chrysolampis mosquitus	♀	3·5	*Coeligena wilsoni*	♀	7·5
Hylocharis leucotis II	♂	3·5	*Coeligena torquata*	♂	7·5
Amazilia iodura	♂	4·0	*Colibri coruscans*	♂	8·5
Amazilia franciae	♀	4·5	*Heliodoxa rubinoides*	♂	9·0
Amazilia tzacatl	♂	4·5	*Eutoxeres aquila*	♂	10·0
Colibri cyanotus	♂	5·0	*Ensifera ensifera*	♂	12·0

♂ = male ♀ = female

In some species the males were larger and heavier than the females; in others the reverse was true; in many cases there was no difference between the sexes. Differences may have been due to purely individual factors and not necessarily to differences between the sexes. The net result was yet another mystery of nature, but all in all, they were measured, weighed and found very light.

High-performance aircraft with head and heart

Hummingbirds with their long bills and long tail feathers look wonderfully slender and elegant. But visualise them without these and the power and compression of their bodily structure is apparent. The thorax is formed of a fine filigree basketwork of thin but tough ribs – to refer to them as bones in this context seems to be far-fetched. In medium-sized hummingbird species the thorax has a diameter of about a third of an inch. The astonishingly high breastbone projects far forwards. A third of an inch high, thin as a razor-blade but tough and elastic, it serves for the attachment and support of the breast musculature which is over a third of an inch thick.

Hummingbird species with short tails, as for example *Acestrura mulsanti* or *Calothorax lucifer*, have an enchantingly chubby appearance. As they travel through the air, humming and whirring at great speed, their plumpness gives them a distinctly jovial appearance. Their speed and the noise of their wings are indicative of the power of the muscle motor that drives the little airship forwards.

The heart, which has to provide this powerful motor with fuel, almost fills the entire thorax and is relatively the largest of all those of the warm-blooded animals. It beats 500 to 1,200 times per minute depending on circumstances. Because the hummingbird can only use a light, 'highly explosive' fuel for such a finely tuned motor, the food must be correspondingly easy to digest. The short, extremely thin tube of the alimentary canal scarcely adds anything to their weight.

These birds spend most of the time on the wing and so do not rely much on their legs. These are short, with three toes in front and one behind, and have long, sharp claws. As in the European swift they serve only for perching and, when necessary, for fighting. (And fights take place every day.)

Their thin pointed bills, usually long, are a particularly noteworthy feature. It is immediately apparent that the bill is a fine, specialised tool, like forceps or minute tubes; the hummingbird's bill has no similarity to the seed-cracking bills of some song birds or the powerful cutting and piercing weapons of insect-eaters or indeed of birds of prey. Nature has supplied hummingbirds with instruments for quite specific purposes. The bill is a proper probe that can be introduced deep into narrow openings. But the length and external appearance of the bill are not sufficient alone to achieve the purpose for which nature designed the feeding mechanism of hummingbirds.

The first time anyone sees a hummingbird's long white tongue protruding from its bill he always expresses astonishment. The tongue extends so far forward – sometimes it is longer than the bill itself – that there seems no end to it. One cannot help wondering how it is possible for any bird to stick its tongue so far out.

The base of the tongue is embedded in a meshwork of fine muscle. The long muscular strands of the hyoid apparatus support the tongue's far-reaching movement. These muscles run from behind up over the bird's skull, and it is possible to watch them in action.

Some hummingbirds, weakened by a long journey, have to be held in the hand and encouraged to drink. The tip of the bill is dipped into the food solution until, stimulated by damp and taste, the bird starts to work its tongue. It is possible to tell when it starts to drink and for how long it continues from the rapid rhythmical movements of its head feathers, which result from the action of the muscles that propel the hyoid apparatus backwards and forwards. (If a newly arrived bird drinks, one can consider oneself lucky because, immediately after drinking, the apparently sick and dying bird will fly away as though it had nothing the matter with it. It is a good idea therefore to shut the window beforehand.)

Later one can also see the tip of the tongue in action. Normally the bird does not dip the tip of the bill in the food solution. Its tongue is divided at the tip like a snake's. The two tiny points have fine fringes directed inwards which soak up the liquid diet and dispatch it into the fine grooves which run backwards from the centre of the tongue.

Even when drinking very greedily a hummingbird does not forget to keep an eye on its surroundings. They have relatively large black eyes which look as though they are taking everything in; their vision is acute and very small insects are perceived at great distances. They can look at you so attentively that you cannot help feeling that they are intelligent, and it is easy to accept the evidence of those ornithologists who have established that the weight of a hummingbird's brain in relation to its body weight is relatively larger than that of most other birds.

The wings, which are constructed in the same way in all species of hummingbird, are significantly different from those of other birds. Sparrows, swallows, storks, gulls, jungle fowl and pelicans all

33

fly by making use of the whole arm, the upper and lower arm as well as the hand. The primary feathers are fairly evenly spaced. The size and area of the total wing surface varies in these birds but this is the only difference in wing structure among them.

By contrast, the upper and lower arms in hummingbirds are so short – albeit strong and closely applied to the body – that one could say that the bird flies only with its hands. Ten long, narrow, stiff primary feathers give to the wing the vibrating character of an insect's wing.

But, of course, hummingbirds are not insects. They possess the characteristic that differentiates birds from all other animals: feathers. And what feathers! When a hummingbird shoots into the light, whirring through the air at an appropriate angle to the observer, there is a really brilliant firework display of iridescent feathers. No other bird possesses ornamental feathers that light up to such an extent.

Tanagers, honey-eaters and exotic starlings certainly have areas of plumage which shine like varnish and silk, but hummingbird feathers are aflame; their fiery light is comparable to the luminescence of a glow-worm, although the effect is due to quite different causes. The whole spectrum of the sun, with all the colours of the rainbow, appear on these feathers. The iridescence is retained throughout the whole year. Many of the females also have this jewel-like ornamentation and are indistinguishable from the males. Some females and some males, however, are inconspicuous.

In relation to their body surface hummingbirds have the densest plumage of all birds – the individual feathers have been counted. The feathers lie tight against the body, almost without down. It is difficult to blow the feathers aside when examining these birds. The wing feathers are faintly metallic in all hummingbirds and have a black or blackish-brown coloration. To the joy of all taxidermists these little birds have very tough and resistant skin. Hummingbirds fight like street urchins – attacking each other with bill and claws – but I have yet to find one with a wound.

This tough skin is useful in general but it was once a disadvantage to the hummingbirds. In the 19th century hundreds of thousands of them were killed and brought to Europe for use in ladies' accessories. Fortunately this enthusiasm, like everything else to do with fashion, has waned, but our joy in the living wonder remains.

34

Secret fire   Lying on the desk in front of me is a feather. It is about half an inch long, a rather small and ordinary looking bird's feather. Neither the white quill, the whitish-grey shaft nor the vane with its barbs is worthy of note. Just towards the base of the shaft there is a warm cushion of dirty grey down. Farther up towards the tip and regularly arranged are the barbs of the vane, first whitish grey, then pale brown, and finally the tip: a semicircular expanse of short, dark brown barbs. As I said, a very ordinary looking feather.

1420366

Admittedly any bird's feather, with its extreme lightness coupled with stability, is a masterpiece of nature but apart from this there is nothing remarkable about the feather lying on my desk. Then, as I start to brush it aside, suddenly there is a ruby-red flash of such intensity that I stop, spell-bound. The small semicircular area of vane at the tip of the feather is aflame like a jewel. The dark brown blob of colour has been transformed into a fiery red.

I step back one or two paces, and then retreat into the passage. Even at a distance of eight to ten yards I can still see these tiny points of light glowing like the snuffed-out tip of a match. Of the rest of the feather – the shaft and the vane, which are much larger than the tip – nothing is to be seen.

When I shift my position, changing the angle of view, the fire is extinguished. Move a single step to the side and it is once more on fire. What exactly is happening?

Many complicated biological and physical factors are involved, but it should be possible to explain the phenomenon by using simple illustrations from which a parallel may be drawn.

Isaac Newton, the English physicist, mathematician and astronomer who lived two hundred and fifty years ago, investigated the nature of light and discovered the force of gravity. He was the first to observe the colour rings of thin plates or lamellae, which have been named Newton's rings after him. In his work *Optics* he wrote that the iridescence of birds' feathers was similar to the colours caused by the reflexion of light from thin plates. The phenomenon, which we observe in soap-bubbles or in films of oil on water, is seen many times more strongly in hummingbird's feathers. Their special structure diffracts the light in such a way as to produce what are known as structural colours.

Feathers consist of a horny substance known as keratin. In hummingbirds the finest branches of the feather, the barbules, which

35

hold the vane together with their hooklets and yet allow it elasticity, are covered with microscopically thin, colourless, horny lamellae. In the Ruby-throated Hummingbird each lamella is only 1/4000 of a millimetre thick. My fingers are unfortunately too clumsy and my eyesight too poor to lift one of these miniature reflectors from its feather barbule and measure its thickness.

The scientist Jean Dorst has accomplished this feat. He too confesses that he had difficulties in making the measurements and this one can well believe. These lamellae can just be seen under an ordinary microscope. They form a system of superimposed layers and there are many variations in the position of the lamellae relative to one another.

In order to see them clearly, the observer as well as the light source and the object must be in a certain position. If one alters the angle of view slowly, the colour changes and passes through the complete spectrum, from dark red, pale red through gold and golden-yellow to a beautiful green. Under the electron microscope, with magnifications of forty to fifty thousand times, it is possible to see that the lamellae consist of air-filled, elliptical cells, which break up the light like millions of tiny soap-bubbles and reflect it as violet, blue, green or golden rays.

The small ornamental feathers, which have their metallic parts in the outer third of their length, lie one above the other like the tiles on a roof, in such a way that their iridescent parts are visible. They may be so close together that a whole area of feathers may appear as a single smooth shiny plate of metal. It is only on closer inspection that one sees, depending on the species of hummingbird, a granular structure of the surface; this appears to be set with numerous diamond chips, or it shows patterns like tiny wafers, as though made of chased gold or hammered copper and lit from within.

When I sprayed my hummingbirds with water the iridescent green on the head of a Blue-throated Sylph then changed to just as intense a bright red. A Ruby-and-topaz Hummingbird, which has a golden breast and throat when dry, changes when wet into a bird with ruby-red plumage. Dorst has also investigated this phenomenon. He attributes it to the thickness of the individual lamellae. The thicker they become – and they swell in water – the longer the wavelength becomes. The result is a different colour. The shorter the wavelength the more the colour changes to blue and violet tones, the longer it is the more the colour changes through green and yellow to red.

The more ordinary colours of birds' feathers, the pigmentary colours, are caused by the presence of coloured chemical substances, such as melanin or carotenoid. They are not iridescent nor do their colours change or disappear completely when they are seen from different angles. For example, the tail feathers of budgerigar, which appear blue owing to the presence of air-filled 'box–cells' may be shiny but they are not iridescent.

In addition to feathers with structural colours, hummingbirds also have pigmented areas in the plumage. The Frilled Coquette, *Lophornis magnifica*, is the model example of a hummingbird with every conceivable type of colour and ornamentation. Its chestnut crest is pigmented like that of a Red Cardinal. The forehead and throat, on the other hand, are a brilliant iridescent green, owing to structural coloration. The 'frill' of long plumes at the sides of the neck are pure white, but they are dusted over at the tips with a delicate green iridescence. When erected, the frill looks like a beautiful Japanese fan. The body is brownish with a burnished gold effect and the tail feathers, arranged in a fan, have a rich pigmentation which gives them an intense brown colour. Here nature has been at great pains to employ several different principles in the adornment of a tiny bird.

Viewing this dazzling display one has to admit that humans are at a disadvantage in this respect. The representatives of our fair sex seemed to recognise this lack of brilliance when they adorned themselves with hummingbird feathers.

The marvel of hummingbird flight

*Rockets and
aerial acrobatics*

The first thing that struck me about *Calothorax lucifer* was its flight. I collected the bird from the Lufthansa authorities in Munich in a transport container, a light structure about twice the size of a small bird-cage. Instead of wire-mesh it had canvas walls and a bottom made of light metal. A clean white cord, a kind of curtain line, had been stretched across the cage to provide the bird with perching facilities.

But *Calothorax lucifer* appeared to ignore the cord, the floor, the grating of fine mesh and indeed every kind of perch. It hung poised in the air at the geometrical centre-point of its enclosure and looked at me. Its body was not much larger than that of a Privet Hawk-moth. In fact it reminded me of this moth. It was similarly coloured and had the same squat body. Its long, slightly curved bill looked like an extended proboscis. Of its wings only a vibrating shadow was to be seen.

It buzzed like a hornet and performed a series of astonishing flight manoeuvres, hovering and turning on one spot, travelling forwards and backwards and sideways; sometimes it progressed cautiously, almost in a dignified manner and at other times it suddenly shot off like a toy rocket. Moving up and down it investigated the walls and every corner carefully but never bumped against anything. Every ten minutes or so it went to the feeding-bottle hanging in the box, but it did so without haste. When drinking it sometimes left off, raised its head and looked calmly around.

Although it was continuously in flight all this took place without the slightest sign of breathlessness or fatigue. The bird also showed no signs of alarm. When I raised my hand it only gazed at me. There was nothing of the nervous, panic fluttering of other birds.

I carried the container to the car and placed it beside me on the seat. Because I drove slowly, so as not to shake the feeding solution and to give the bird a chance to drink, it took me a good hour to get home. *Calothorax* covered the whole distance in non-stop flight.

38

Later on, its powers of endurance were to drive me nearly mad when I was trying to photograph it.

When I released it into the aviary I was apprehensive lest the other larger species of hummingbird should attack it and keep it from feeding. Humming all the time, it flew around energetically, carefully testing the local surroundings. Its drone was so impressive that the other species in the aviary did not molest it. The latter included a bold *Amazilia* and species of *Aglaiocercus* and *Boissonneaua*. These species, although longer than the *Calothorax*, moved respectfully to one side and behaved like a canary when a wasp approaches.

The droning made by this very tiny hummingbird was remarkably reminiscent of a flying insect. Although the technique of flight and the structure of the wings are similar in all hummingbirds, the very small ones fly differently from the medium-sized and large species. Their wings are somewhat shorter in proportion to the length of the body. In the Bee Hummingbird, the longest wing feather scarcely reaches to the end of the body, whereas in the other species it exceeds the body length by a good third. The dwarfs shoot over great distances at the speed of an arrow, in a straight line and dead on target. As one cannot see the vibrating wings these birds look like tiny rockets or, when travelling slowly, like squat little airships.

The larger species – one must not forget that they are also small – give a really breath-taking acrobatic performance. They hover, dive, whirl forwards, upwards, backwards and sideways; they remain stationary in the air, turn on to their backs, stand head up or upside down in the air, so that one can scarcely believe one's eyes. The way in which these birds master their element, the air, is phenomenal. We are so accustomed to thinking in terms of conventional flight, drawing comparisons with other birds and with our own flying techniques, that we are bewildered by the aerobatic performances of hummingbirds.

Even if there were hundreds of different ways of moving about, the hummingbird's flying technique would still be the most astonishing of all. For thousands of years man has longed to move freely in three dimensions and, although he has succeeded in inventing many different kinds of flying machines, in hummingbirds he can see perfection in the art of flying.

39

The wings start to vibrate while the bird is still perching. It does not take off with a leap, but merely releases the grip of its claws, rises vertically into the air and flies. With the body in a horizontal position it whirls like a helicopter, but it can also shoot straight up like a rocket.

It chooses its perch always with a view to having sufficient space in which to fly. It never perches on the ground unless forced to do so. It uses neither camouflage nor hiding place but relies entirely on its wings. If a predatory bird swoops from above, it allows itself to fall and conquers its element in the manner of a parachutist.

When surprised by a sudden attack from the front, it turns on to its back, virtually throwing its neck above its head and shoots off in this 'impossible' position, does a roll and then flies off normally – an astonishingly evasive manoeuvre which must be exceptionally discouraging to any attacker. On finding that a hummingbird can lead with its tail and fly off backwards, the attacker retires from the scene and does not ever try again to match itself against a hummingbird.

One day my Blue-throated Sylph decided to begin building a nest on a branch right up against the wall. The approach to the branch was perfectly convenient from the front but it was impossible for the bird to turn round once it was there. It could not even perch comfortably and was forced to hold its head and bill up in the air. It would emerge backwards from its roosting place hidden under leaves, travelling backwards like an aeroplane reversing out of a hangar. It always made a most attractive picture as it floated up from perch, moving out backwards, with its tail leading the way. Many hummingbirds choose covered places to sleep in; in the evening they enter by flying in forwards, and in the morning they leave by flying out backwards.

Opposite: Aerial acrobats in action. Above: a female Ruby-Topaz Hummingbird travelling at full speed. Below left: taking a corner at speed. A female *Anthracothorax nigricollis* tries to avoid the photographic trip, noticed at the last moment. Below right: a female Blue-tailed Emerald, *Chlorostilbon mellisugus*, flying upside down in a somersault.

When a hummingbird is flying straight ahead, its body lies horizontally on the air cushion. The flight may be in a straight line or undulating. The bird glides for short periods in between the whirring action of the wings. This variant, however, is not comparable to the sailing of a swallow or gull, but is more like the motorless flight of a jet fighter. Travelling at high velocity, the bird takes short rests in mid-air before going full speed again.

I observed this method of flying when a *Colibri cyanotus*, escaped

40

Fast braking action. Left: forward flight. Right: emergency stop in the air. With head drawn in, tail feathers fully expanded and wings in reverse, the bird stops immediately. Above: *Lesbia victoriae* ♀. Below: *Heliodoxa rubinoides* ♂.

Above: The iridescence of the feathers is caused by the refraction of light. A male Long-billed Starthroat, *Heliomaster longirostris* (Paraguay), a little bored by my photographic efforts, shows the effect of the refraction of the light rays. Seen from the side the throat and head look dark.

Below: Seen from the front – another angle of vision – the light is refracted and reflected, and the feathers show their iridescence. The sudden flashes are enchanting.

from my aviary and went buzzing off to my neighbour's border of phlox. After I had hung up a few red feeding-bottles in my garden it returned and remained for several days feeding, visiting flowers and hunting insects, a green and blue envoy from South America shimmering in our sun. Then it disappeared (Cost £16 [$45] without upkeep).

When seen in forward flight a hummingbird looks like any other bird except for the remarkably fast vibration of its wings. Its flying technique, however, is completely different.

Instant braking

One cannot fail to be astonished every time a hummingbird in full flight stops dead with a jolt. If an aeroplane tried to imitate this trick it would surely lose the wings, tail, engine and all accessories, including the pilot. Whereas a buzzard swooping requires a distance of several yards to pull up, a hummingbird stops on the spot without any braking distance.

A hummingbird is very light, it seems to be only 'feathers and wings'. It can stop immediately in mid-air if it suddenly turns into a cross wind. It does this by holding its long wings and the big surface area of the expanded tail against the current of air and at the same time rotating its wings backwards – the latter action being the special feature of a hummingbird. Since no other bird can fly backwards, the fast brakes of the hummingbird are, so to speak, its own patent.

The best helicopter

Superlative after superlative. There is no other bird which can fly so competently when stationary. It is true that falcons, sunbirds and a few other genera are able to hover, but they look awkward and clumsy as they flutter and shake. The hummingbird does not shake nor is it jarred. The body is held quite still in the air. The fascinating thing about its hovering is the smooth, helicopter-like vibration of its wings, which apparently have no 'dead spots' – both the upward and downward strokes being powered and even at high vibrations the body does not shake. It can stop and turn at will. It can stay in the air in an upright, diagonal or horizontal position.

Even the position of the head does not affect it. Flowers can be harvested from in front, above or below; leaves can be examined from all angles; nest material is picked up, pulled out and woven in any conceivable fashion and in any position. All this takes place in

Opposite: Forward and backward flight by a female Andean Emerald, *Amazilia franciae* (Venezuela). Left: forward take-off and flight. The wings start to vibrate while the bird is still perching. They remain extended and do not flex even in the upstroke. Right: taking off and flying backwards. The peculiar joint of the hummingbird's wing allows the wing surface to turn through 180 degrees. This enables the bird to fly backwards.

45

flight and apparently without effort or fatigue. When it is hovering, the tail-feathers play scarcely any part. Hummingbirds that have lost their tail-feathers keep their balance just as well. The tail-feathers are a great help – although not essential – for small quick adjustments of height, for braking, cornering and fast backward acceleration. When hovering, the long-tailed species keep their tail-feathers motionless, either stretched out straight or slightly raised.

Some of the smaller species have an amusing way of flicking their tails actively when hovering. I do not subscribe to the view that these are balancing movements. A hummingbird always keeps its balance by means of its vibrating wings which support it and make corrections for the body in any position.

The tail flicking is a matter of temperament, a charming attribute like the tail-wagging movements of a Redstart. My wife claims that hummingbirds also wink, but this is going too far, in my opinion.

Fish or bird? When a hummingbird flies slowly through the branches and between leaves, giving the impression of slow-motion movie film, its wings are practically invisible; its body glides smoothly forwards and the bird appears to be floating miraculously in the air. The effect in the long-tailed species is particularly entrancing.

It is the slowness of the movement which strikes one. Visitors, who at first sight mistook my glass cage for an aquarium, thought that they were looking at a beautiful and rare fish swimming behind the panes. The impression created by this movement is the same.

Nose dive Who knows what the bird has spotted when from a smooth flight it suddenly shoots up vertically for several yards, like a rocket, and then makes a breathtaking nose dive. The bird does not fold its wings and allow itself to fall like a stone; it is not satisfied by the speed of the fall, on the contrary, it reinforces the fall, increasing the speed to well above sixty miles per hour, by accelerating the rate of vibration of the wings. The humming increases to what is almost a hiss, indeed in one species (*Selasphorus platycercus*) with specially shaped wing tips it becomes a loud whistle. Two inches from the ground the dive stops abruptly – it seems as though the wings must break – and already the bird is on its way up again.

It is impossible to describe what happens when one hummingbird

46

chases another. The normal speed is doubled, trebled, and all that one sees of two tiny, iridescent bodies is the line of flight in the air. The chase goes on through branches, between leaves and a hair's breadth from tree trunks and rocks, but they never even so much as brush against any obstacle.

How they catch flies Hummingbirds show the same skill when hunting insects. The way this is done depends on the species, its appetite and the supply of insects.

Boissonneaua prefers to fly out from a familiar perch, making mostly short sallies after flies buzzing by and then returning immediately to its branch. If a *Hylocharis* has eaten no flies for a long time and suddenly sees a swarm, it dives in without hesitation, strikes out while hovering to left and right, forwards and upwards – rarely downwards – and begins to snap them up. Almost every strike means the end of a fly, which disappears into its wide-open jaws. Every hummingbird of about thirty species which I have observed continuously from close range snaps up flies like a swallow. The idea that they shoot them with the tongue, like a tree-frog or a chameleon, fastening them with 'glue', or even seize them with the fringe of the forked tongue, is not correct.

Chrysolampis mosquitus usually takes the flies off the window-panes with the tip of the bill, like forceps. From this position, however, approaching the fly from the rear, it is not possible to dispatch the insect immediately: it tosses the prey back from the tip of the bill into the jaws, swinging its whole body backwards while in flight. *Amazilia tzacatl* proceeds in the same way. An *Amazilia franciae*, whose upper mandible tip had been broken, could not take any flies from the window-pane or from a leaf, in spite of repeated attempts. But with a sticky tongue and the tree-frog technique it could have done so without any difficulty. I examined all my hummingbirds to see whether the tongue is sticky enough to be able to hold a fruitfly. In the interests of science, I opened their bills and placed one of these small flies on the tongue with a pair of forceps. Although I pressed the fly slightly down, it fell off as soon as I tilted the bill.

Hummingbirds must therefore operate by the same technique as members of the swallow family. This involves considerable skill and agility. The bird usually hovers behind and below the flying

47

insect and catches it by suddenly shooting forwards and upwards. The jaws work like a landing-net. All that is left for the bird to do is to swallow it. If it misses the insect it tries to catch it while it is still in the air, making a lightning dive. But if the insect has fallen to the ground the bird takes no further notice of it.

If the insect remains in flight after the bird's initial failure, as may happen, the bird continues the chase until it has caught it. In these circumstances the bird's virtuosity in the air is fully demonstrated. It selects an individual insect and then follows exactly every twist and turn made by the prey, until the hunt is successfully concluded.

Although it will also take sitting flies, small spiders and tiny bugs with the tips of its bill, it seems to prefer to catch its prey on the wing. With fruitflies that are crawling about on a banana it adopts shock tactics and tries to startle the flies into taking off. It increases its wing vibrations, spreads its tail-feathers and hangs in the air, close above or in front of the flies, until one of them takes off and is caught.

Courtship flight — Whatever the accomplishments of hummingbirds, they can impress neither their mates nor anyone else by their song. When they want to arouse the interest of the opposite sex, they have to do something specially elaborate: they fly.

The flight repertoire with which the male dazzles the female is overwhelming even for a lady hummingbird who certainly knows something about flight. The male courts the female, vibrating his wings at their highest frequency, as she sits on her perch. He displays his metallic colours from their most favourable angle, showing them off to their best advantage, and he swings about in front of her so fast that the eye can scarcely follow. Suddenly he shoots sixty feet up into the air, allows himself to fall, halts the mad dive immediately in front of the female and shoots up again; diving and swinging to and fro he even sings – if one can call it singing – and continues his capers until, impressed and bewildered, she surrenders completely.

One can also observe this display flight in an aviary. Once acclimatised, hummingbirds behave completely naturally. My two *Hylocharis leucotis* gave an indefatigable display of U-turns in front of the females of their choice, flying up to the ceiling and down again, almost touching them each time as they dived down to

48

where the females were perching. One chose a female of his own species, the other a female *Chrysolampis mosquitus*.

If another male, even a larger one, crossed their path they attacked it resolutely. They chased after it like arrows shot from a bow, trying to drive the opponent away by spectacular flight displays, hovering, lying flat in the air, tail spread, bill stuck out, with fast wing vibrations and quick swings back and forth.

If the adversary still appeared unalarmed they went at it full tilt. They looked like two fencers facing each other with drawn foils, lunging, withdrawing and making serious efforts to strike the opponent. The victor in such aerial combats was always the more daring attacker and the superior flier was also the more successful with the females.

The bird drill It seems incredible that a bird in flight can spin on its own axis like a small top. When an *Amazilia tzacatl* wanted to open the calyx of a flower hanging down, it approached the bloom from above and virtually became a flying drill. It positioned its bill over the flower and then spun quickly on its own axis until it had bored a hole.

During a series of experiments I tried offering a tiny *Calothorax* a rather bitter food solution. As the bird had been kept short of food before the experiment, it naturally flew keenly and unsuspectingly to its favourite feeding-bottle. It had scarcely applied its bill when it drew back a good eighteen inches and spun round like a child's top in order to toss away the bitter tasting solution.

Its hunger drove it once again to the 'filling station'. It took a sip, pulled back and again went spinning round, to such an extent that I thought it would never stop. After several attempts it took the food, presumably under the dictum 'feed or die', but it behaved as though it was offended for the rest of the day.

Landing without breaking the eggs Hummingbirds land the same way as they take off. They come down at full speed, landing abruptly, or descend more gently, hovering. The wings continue to vibrate when their toes are still grasping the branch.

A female lowers herself on to her nest without using her feet. No helicopter pilot could land more accurately, more gently, or more carefully than this little bird as she hovers down on to her eggs or young. Even when the nest lies hidden under a natural roof, a leaf or

49

a large flower, the bird flies in with such precision that it does not even touch the edge of the nest. It sinks down into the little hollow as though landing in a feather bed.

Solution of the problem: double power output

The flying efficiency and manoeuvrability of this family of birds are so far ahead of the known techniques in the field of aeronautics that scientists have been particularly keen to investigate the secrets of hummingbird flight.

'Like a helicopter!' everyone says who sees a hummingbird hovering in one position. Any child knows what a helicopter is, but what does the dictionary say?

'A helicopter is an aircraft which is capable of taking off and landing vertically; it can also remain stationary in the air. Instead of supporting surfaces a helicopter has large, horizontally arranged, motor-driven rotors which produce lift and forward propulsion at the same time.'

The rotors of a hummingbird are its wings. We first see how they work when the bird is stationary in the air, looking like an elongated, vibrating shadow which lies horizontally in the air.

Seen from the side the wing-beat describes a flattened figure of eight. More than a thousand photographs of hummingbirds in hovering flight show that the wing tips are always directed forwards, backwards or sideways, never upwards or downwards. On the other hand, ten photographs of a fluttering sunbird showed four positions with the wings directed downwards.

The wings of a hovering hummingbird beat forwards and backwards, not up and down like those of other birds. Since they describe a figure of eight there is no 'dead spot' in the movement. Result: uninterrupted, vibration-free movement and a steadily held body position even at high-frequency wing-beats. The body may be held in a vertical, horizontal or oblique position. The figure of eight described by the wings is always horizontal.

From this it follows that the wings must be seated in a movable joint. The anatomy confirms this supposition. The mechanism of this short but powerful articulation, consisting of shoulder and elbow joint, is unique and enables the bird to fly even with the upperside of the wings facing downwards.

This is the true secret of hummingbird flight. Whether the bird is hovering in one position or flying backwards, with each lift of the

50

wing, it tips the front edge backwards, so that power is maintained on the downstroke and on the upstroke of the wing, regardless of whether the bird is the right way up in the air or upside down.

One must visualise each wing as a long, flat, rigid rudder, which can be swung backwards and forwards on its long axis. First the under surface of the blade then the upper surface works against the resistance.

The hands of a swimmer lying on his back in the water execute similar movements to those of the hummingbird's wings; he keeps himself afloat by paddling his hands to and fro. Exercising a powerful thrust with one hand or the other, he can steer himself at will, moving backwards or sideways while afloat.

In backwards flight the wings of the hummingbird twist even more strongly than when hovering. They are swung forwards like the arms and hands of a man who wants to hug another person. They are pulled back with the palms of the hands, so to speak, facing upwards and these movements provide the back thrust.

When the hummingbird shoots forwards its body lies flat on the air cushion. In this position the wing-beat operates as in any other bird. But in the subsequent upstroke the wing is not flexed at the wrist and elbow joint in order to avoid the resistance of the air, nor are the primaries spread. The wings do in fact remain rigid on the upstroke. The rear edge of the wing is, however, lowered a little. In this way the upward stroke of the wings also gives forward thrust.

It is clear that the wings must form a unique, firm and yet yielding surface in order to present sufficient resistance to the air pressure with both the upper and lower surfaces. Fine hooklets link the feather barbules together. With this rigid wing structure it does not matter whether the upperside is facing downwards or upwards. From the point of view of flight technique it is also immaterial whether the bird is positioned in the air on its back or on its belly, or whether its head is up or down. By allowing the wings to rotate through the figure of eight course, the remarkable articulation enables the body to be held in any position the bird likes.

It can switch from forward to backward flight in a fraction of a second. The human eye is incapable of perceiving the rotation of the wings. Not even a very fast slow-motion camera can make this movement visible. We see only the body moving swiftly backwards.

51

The wings of an ordinary bird work like a two-stroke engine. The downstroke does the work and the upstroke merely lifts the wing into a position where it can be powered again.

The hummingbird is, so to speak, the only mass-produced single-stroke engine in the world. Both the downstroke and the upstroke are powered. It generates drive with both strokes, thereby doubling the output. The hummingbird engine is virtually an almost perfect forerunner of the variable speed engine with its smooth performance and economic utilisation of energy. The result of this double action is an explosive acceleration and a speed that is astonishing for so small a bird.

With stopwatch and stroboscope

Looking at a hummingbird slowly floating through the air like a lurking dragonfly, one cannot help thinking that it should be possible to catch it like a butterfly. In fact the bird allows the net to come within a bill's length – with malicious glee or so it seems – and then all at once there is a rising hum. What was a peacefully floating bird shoots off as a flickering point, like a tracer bullet. To measure accurately the speed of a hummingbird, a tiny object with a propensity for abruptly changing tempo and direction, presents real problems. It is much more difficult, for example, than timing a pigeon which follows a straight course uniformly and on target over long distances. It is not surprising, therefore, that one hears differing reports on the speed of hummingbirds. They vary from thirty to ninety miles per hour.

Two observers, Hayes (1929) and Allard (1934), were able by chance to compare the speed of the tiny Ruby-throated Hummingbird with that of their vehicles. One recorded forty-four miles per hour and the other fifty-nine miles per hour. Unfortunately we do not know whether there was any wind on these days and if so its strength and from which direction it blew. This represents an unknown factor in the test. In addition the accuracy of a speedometer is not to be trusted within the odd five to ten miles or so per hour.

In 1945 Wagner timed the speed of a *Colibri thalassimus* which was performing courtship flights between two trees; he relied on his watch and reported the average speed to be fifty-five miles per hour. He reckoned that two hummingbirds chasing each other reached a speed as high as ninety miles per hour.

52

These are astonishing speeds, scarcely credible when one thinks that even fast-flying insects travel only nine to twelve miles per hour and ordinary song-birds twenty-eight miles per hour at the most. In order to obtain the most accurate figures possible, the American ornithologist Greenewalt subjected the small Ruby-throated Hummingbird (*Archilochus colubris*) to a tough test. He allowed the bird to struggle against the adjustable air-stream in a wind tunnel equipped with a feeding-bottle.

In this ingenious construction – 'Daddy's torture chamber', as Greenewalt's children disrespectfully named it – the bird attained a speed of twenty-nine miles per hour. Its wing tips described almost a semicircle and it could scarcely have made higher upstrokes or deeper downstrokes. It is still an open question whether the fifty-three beats per second represented its maximum. If the bird was in good condition with satisfactory reserves of energy and it found the current of air required too much effort to make the attempt to reach the food worthwhile, it could well afford to forgo a meal; in this case it could give up before testing its strength to the utmost. Alternatively, if its condition was poor or became so – hummingbirds become exhausted very quickly – it would not have the strength to give its maximum performance. In addition there are far stronger driving factors than the stimulus of reaching a food site, for example, aggressive pursuit and the mad manoeuvres of the courtship flight.

I was able to make precise observations of the daily chase of two Blue-throated Sylphs, *Aglaiocercus kingi*, during the courtship period. They flew through the aviary on a standard route, with almost geometrical precision, sometimes eight to twelve times in succession without stopping. The course that they followed was an elongated slightly sloping figure of eight. The direction of the route was dictated by the need to avoid tropical vegetation and consequently the manoeuvring of the leading bird, to evade the pursuer, was almost always the same.

Making a high-pitched humming sound they shot diagonally upwards, dropping headlong into the first bend and dived diagonally down, heading with terrifying audacity on a collision course straight for the opposite wall and drawing up with only inches to spare. Turning in a way that nobody would believe possible, unless they had seen it for themselves, they were back on the return route forthwith, wings humming and piping loudly.

53

From a distance of fifteen feet these slender, long-tailed birds hurtling through the air did not look like two bodies, with outlines that were even vaguely recognisable; instead they resembled green and blue iridescent arrows making a single track which suddenly flashed with light. They chashed each other like live miniature devils, apparently regarding this fast game of chance as only a harmless entertainment.

The precision and regularity of their flight allowed me to use a stopwatch, a precision instrument calibrated in tenths of a second. I timed the birds over the same route on more than thirty occasions. The course, which was sometimes circumnavigated as much as eight times in succession had a total length of 73·680 yards, including all the corners and curves.

The two Blue-throated Sylphs flew, if not a world record, then certainly a European indoor record. The conditions of the day: temperature 24° Centigrade (75° F), humidity fifty-five per cent, no wind. The following times were recorded on the first ten occasions; subsequent records showed much the same results on average. From a flying start the leader's time in transit:

1. 3·6 sec. = 42·0 mph		6. 4·2 sec. = 36·1 mph
2. 4·2 sec. = 36·1 mph		7. 3·3 sec. = 45·8 mph
3. 3·2 sec. = 47·2 mph		8. 3·8 sec. = 39·8 mph
4. 4·8 sec. = 31·5 mph		9. 5·1 sec. = 29·7 mph
5. 4·0 sec. = 37·6 mph		10. 3·9 sec. = 38·5 mph

Mean: 38·4 miles per hour

This speed was attained over a short course with several turns in it. It is reasonable to assume that on a straight course the Blue-throated Sylph would have flown faster and might have reached a speed of forty to fifty-five miles per hour. One should remember that this speed is achieved by a tiny, feathered, warm-blooded body weighing only 6 grams. It is equivalent to a flight at fifty-five miles per hour on the roof of a stunting sports aeroplane.

From time to time an African Variable Sunbird (*Cinnyris venustus falkensteini*), took part in the race of the Blue-throated Sylphs. About the size of a tit, this honey-eater is a good flier but it reached a speed of only twenty-three miles per hour, although it was much heavier and stronger than the hummingbird. The sunbird looked like a heavy bomber, effortlessly overtaken by the super-fast manoeuvrable fighter plane, the hummingbird.

54

The most remarkable feature of the flight of hummingbirds is the vibrating wing-beats which are not discernible to the eye. The variation in the number of wing-beats given by different species of so-called ordinary birds and by various insects is indeed remarkable. A swan for instance raises and lowers its wings one and a half times per second. A sparrow achieves thirteen fluttering beats. A bee's wings vibrate at about one hundred and ninety per second. The high-pitched buzz of a mosquito – a vibration level that is almost painful to our ears – is caused by wing beats at the rate of five hundred per second.

In 1951 Edgerton, Niedrach and Van Rieper measured up to two hundred wing-beats per second in the courtship flights of *Archilochus colubris* and *Selasphorus rufus*. This is a fantastic number. One of my smallest hummers, *Calothorax lucifer*, almost forced a pane of glass (15 feet by 6 feet) from its frame in the front of the aviary, purely as a result of the vibration of its wings. Improbable as this may sound it happens to be true. The huge sheet of glass was originally not very firmly anchored and at a certain high frequency of the wing-beats, the pane started to vibrate a little, then increasingly strongly, until it vibrated so hard that the screws and angle-iron were torn away with such a loud crack that the plaster fell down from the ceiling. At first the little creature was considerably alarmed by this unexpected accompaniment to its humming. Later on it appeared to have deliberately worked out the critical frequency at which other hummingbirds were intimidated by its noise. In fact a Brown Inca, *Coeligena wilsoni*, which often attacked it, immediately turned away when the rattling began. I had the screws promptly tightened before I was faced with a disaster.

The frequency of wing-beats and other fast, repetitive movements which the eye is unable to perceive, such as quickly rotating machine parts, can be made visible by means of a stroboscope. This speed-measuring device is capable of discharging a thousand or more flickers per second. The desired frequency can be set precisely from zero to fifteen thousand. Each individual flicker of light may last only one hundred-thousandth of a second.

If one lets a hummingbird fly in a dark room and turns on the stroboscope, so that bright flashes begin to light up periodically, the vibrating wings of the flying bird will show up well in the directly

illuminated position. By experimenting, one can set the stroboscope to flash at the same frequency as the wings are beating and one then gets the impression that the bird is hovering with stationary wings. With any tiny alteration of the frequency either of the light flashes or of the wing-beats, the wings again appear to vibrate, slower or faster according to the adjustment of the stroboscope or to the natural variation in the wing-beat frequency. It seemed to me that no hummingbird has ever looked more ethereal than when floating in mid-air, held in the cold blue light of the stroboscope: slowly but ceaselessly beating its wings, slightly relaxing the wing-tips, describing a smooth figure of eight as it hovered, or gliding forward, gently rising and falling with smooth elegance. Finally a moment of pure fantasy when all visible movement ceased – a jewel-like bird, shining blue, green, red, golden or violet, like a glowing comet, defying the laws of gravity, hovering here and there, floating up and down.

This is technical illusion and witchcraft at its best. A number of hummingbirds were used in this experiment. I am glad that none of them showed any sign of alarm during the procedure; and, unlike finches, they did not shoot away in panic and break their skulls.

The visual stroboscopy required much patience and repeated critical scrutiny, because the wing-beats being measured continued at the same frequency only for short periods. It was also necessary to avoid exposing an individual for too long to the bright and flickering stroboscopic light; each experiment had to be spread over several evenings.

Anyone who has experienced the sensation of fear when under heavy fire will readily appreciate that the birds being bombarded with optical and acoustic machine-gun fire only hovered and did not give any aggressive or courtship displays. The following figures therefore refer only to hovering flight in one place:

Wing-beats per second:

		Anthracothorax	
Heliomaster longirostris	♂ 22–23	*nigricollis*	♀ 22–24
Heliomaster longirostris	♀ 22–24	*Florisuga mellivora*	♂ 23–25
		Heliodoxa rubinoides	♂ 26–27

Opposite: A female Collared Inca, *Coeligena torquata*, approaches the tiny opening of the flower calyx of this bromelia with remarkable accuracy. While drinking nectar, it pollinates the flower. Above: forward approach. Below: a forward thrust with the tail feathers, wings folded as for backward flight, and the bird goes out in reverse.

Left: Unfamiliar flowers are approached and thoroughly investigated even though they yield little or no nectar. Above: a male White-necked Jacobin, *Florisuga mellivora* (Ecuador), at a magnolia flower. Centre: with head and bill practically engulfed in the flower, the bird still keeps a watchful eye on the camera.

Below left and right: A female Brown Inca, *Coeligena wilsoni* (Colombia), at a daffodil. The bird hovers in mid-air in front of the flower, repeatedly stopping and going into reverse, examining the bloom before diving in again. A really entrancing performance.

The Sparkling Violet-ear, *Colibri coruscans*, one of the first species ever to reach Europe alive, is also a wonderful aeronaut. When excited it erects two patches of violet feathers like large ears. It is taking the pollen from a flower of *Anthurium* with its long pointed tongue.

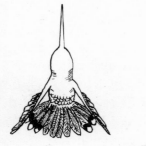

Eutoxeres aquila	♂	26–28	*Chrysolampis mosquitus*	♂	30–32
Amazilia tzacatl	♂	31–34	*Aglaiocercus kingi*	♀	30–32
Hylocharis leucotis II	♂	32–34	*Aglaiocercus kingi*	♂	31–33
Chrysolampis mosquitus	♀	33–35	*Hylocharis leucotis I*	♂	31–33
Colibri cyanotus	♂	34–36	*Amazilia franciae*	♀	36–37
Selasphorus rufus	♀	35–37	*Lesbia victoriae*	♂ & ♀	36–39
Chlorostilbon			*Thalurania watertoni*	♂	37–39
mellisugus	♂ & ♀	36–37	*Damophila julie*	♂	47–49
Boissonneaua jardini	♂	26–29	*Damophila julie*	♀	48–49
Colibri coruscans	♂	27–28	*Popelairia conversii*	♀	64–67
Ensifera ensifera	♂	28–30	*Calothorax lucifer*	♀	72–75
Coeligena wilsoni	♀	29–31	*Acestrura mulsanti*	♂	75–77
Heliothryx barroti	♂	30–31	*Acestrura mulsanti*	♀	76–79

In 1939 Stolpe and Zimmer measured the frequency of wing-beats in the following species:

Eupetomena macruora	21–23	*Chrysolampis mosquitus*	32–33
Melanotrochilus	27–30	*Chlorostilbon*	36–39
Chlorestes notatus	30–33	*Phaethornis ruber*	50–51

Greenewalt reported the following figures:

Patagona gigas		8–10	*Calliphlox amethystina* ♂	80
Calliphlox amethystina ♀	60			

According to my observations, the frequency when hovering varied only slightly. It was dependent upon the wing length of the different species of hummingbird. However the frequency increased proportionately as the length of the wings decreased. The frequency of the beats was also influenced by the physical condition of the individual specimen. Thus my Sword-billed Hummingbird, *Ensifera ensifera*, after an initial illness developed from a feeble flier into a really first-class performer, vibrating very actively and relatively fast. I tape-recorded the wing noises of one of the smallest species, *Popelairia conversii*, and also of a medium-sized species, *Amazilia tzacatl*. I then made these visible with the help of an oscilloscope. The amplitude spectrum obtained in this way revealed

Opposite: For comparison, this is how a 'normal' bird flies, in this case a Variable Sunbird (*Cinnyris venustus falkensteini*) from Africa. On the downbeat the primary feathers are widely separated from each other. On the upward stroke (the right-hand series from below upwards) the wings are bent at the wrist and elbow joints in order to avoid air resistance. On the other hand, the wings of hummingbirds remain rigid in both strokes. By this means their flight becomes faster and more elegant with an acceleration that is almost explosive.

a remarkable phenomenon: when it starts, the hummingbird brings its wings to full speed immediately, to the full frequency that is necessary for hovering. There is no gradual revving-up. This accounts for the sudden, loud hum of a hummingbird taking off, accompanied by an instant lift into the air.

The wing-beats increase quite considerably in quick manoeuvres. One can detect this by listening to the rising pitch of the hum made by the wings. It was not possible, however, to adjust the stroboscope quickly enough to record the speed of these wing-beats. In any case they are several times higher than the figures given.

Another observer, Worth, relied on his sense of perfect pitch to determine the frequency from the sound made by the hum of the wings. He estimated sixty-four beats per second in various unidentified species from the Panama region.

Appollinaire once made the mysterious statement: 'The bird sings with its fingers'. In relation to hummingbirds this remark is no longer enigmatic.

Incredible endurance Everything was ready for the exposure: the camera in position, focus and stop tested, film loaded, light cabinet and relays live, the flash tested, the cassette slide withdrawn. After a long search in a botanic garden, the right flower was found and it made a lovely show as it waited, in position, for a visit from the little *Calothorax lucifer*.

There were two possibilities of getting the bird in the correct focal plane. First, it might automatically operate the light trap as it approached. Secondly, I could release the shutter myself as the bird hovered for a second in front of the flower.

I had great difficulty in catching the bird in the aviary before transferring it to the photographic studio. The aviary had a humid tropical climate, and the little brute buzzed around like a wasp. I had hoped that in the photographic studio, it would fly more sedately and approach the flower in a well-behaved manner, thus enabling me to get a photograph. I could not have been more wrong. The unfamiliar surroundings did not bother it but it could see the aviary and, humming angrily, it began to look for a way out. In principle this could have been all right from my point of view, as sooner or later it would strike the light trap. Unfortunately however it took to circling round immediately below the ceiling

62

where there was no chance it would meet the light ray. I lay or rather stood half stooping, finger on the camera release, eyes glued to the flower in case hunger should induce the bird to come down suddenly. My nerves were already somewhat on edge as a result of the earlier attempt to catch it, my back was starting to ache and I was shaking at the knees.

It seemed to be jeering at me and refused to come down. It cruised about for two hours and exhausted not only my patience but also my nervous energy. The first time that it shot down to the flower I did not react at all; on the other occasions I was either too soon or too late. It avoided the 'magic eye' of the light trap with devilish accuracy, swerving up and away at the last moment.

After three hours the flower capitulated and drooped its petals dejectedly. After four hours I accepted defeat. I had not taken a single picture. The bird had remained in continuous flight, occasionally sipping briefly from the feeding-bottle which I offered it several times.

I gave up in the hope that I would have better luck the following day. But it was only after another two days that I got my first photograph, and it took five days more before I got the picture I wanted. Incidentally, the bird was a female.

There are several examples of remarkable endurance in hummingbirds, an endurance which is all the more astonishing when one appreciates their high wing-beat frequency and special flight technique, which permits no intervals of rest while planing or gliding. We know for example that the tiny Ruby-throated Hummingbird, *Archilochus colubris*, which breeds in summer in the United States east of the Mississippi, crosses the Gulf of Mexico on migration. Small groups have often been seen far out, flying like darting arrows over the open sea or have been observed taking a brief rest on ships' aerials.

One way or another, their flight performance is unique, whether they fly the direct route from Florida to the Yucatan Peninsula, thus covering about five hundred miles without a break, or whether, as I think more probable, they first move south and approach Cuba in a hop of one hundred and fifty miles over the Florida Strait – a phenomenal performance for a tiny bird weighing only two and a half grams.

The fact that Ruby-throats have often been seen during the

63

migration season on the Bahamas and along the coasts of Cuba provides evidence in favour of the latter flight route. Also, the journey over the sea in two stages of about one hundred and twenty to one hundred and fifty miles appears more likely. Nevertheless I am not prepared to say after all my experience with them that hummingbirds are not capable of a five hundred mile non-stop flight.

The little Rufous Hummingbird, *Selasphorus rufus* – another North American species – covers even longer distances. In autumn it sets off from Alaska. Seamen have seen it flying over the inclement Gulf of Alaska, miles from land. The migration of this tiny bird – no longer than a matchstick – along the whole of the west coast of North America is an adventure without parallel. The coastal mountains rise to heights of over 15,000 feet and force the birds either to turn out over the open sea or to climb to 8,000 feet in order to find passes through the mountains. Their innate tenacity enables them to keep going. They negotiate storms by flying in the troughs of waves or low over the ground. They withstand below freezing temperatures in a puzzling way, about which more will be said later.

Starting almost from the Arctic Circle in the region of Mount Logan (19,850 feet) they fly along the whole of the west coast of Canada, over the states of Washington, Oregon and California, passing San Francisco and Los Angeles, then over the five hundred mile Gulf of California and end up in sunny Mexico. All in all, they will have covered some two thousand miles and the following spring they make the return trip. One really must pay tribute to this marvellous feat of strength and endurance. The courage and tenacity of such a tiny creature, weighing no more than a pocket pencil-sharpener, is indeed worthy of our humble admiration.

Energy, food and body temperature

Energy foods
and banquets Boxers and track athletes, sprinters and jumpers, weight-lifters and shot-putters, world-record-holders and Olympic competitors – all these people may be justifiably proud of their physical prowess but the hummingbird outstrips them all in terms of performance. It surpasses all other warm-blooded animals be they human or animal. Every day the hummingbird visits from one thousand to two thousand flowers, giving proof of an energy that seems positively astounding to us. A sprinter who wanted to give the same perform-ance, relative to his body weight, would need to produce forty horsepower and to achieve a speed of ninety miles per hour. If a man with this energy output and heat production did evaporate his heat through perspiration his temperature would rise to well over 750° F. This amount of energy, reckoned in thermal units, would correspond to 155,000 calories per day. With his mere 3,000 calories man is left a long way behind.

Where does this little bird get such strength? It is true that its driving power – the flight musculature which is a third of its body weight – is the strongest of any bird. But however powerful a machine is, it will not take you across continents if the correct fuel is lacking. There are several materials that man employs to produce heat and energy for motion. In a fast locomotive this may be coal. A motor-car needs petroleum, a more easily digested food, so to speak, that is richer in calories.

Among the fuels that we take into our bodies as energy-giving food there are fast and slow burners. After consuming a large juicy helping of roast pork we are overtaken by an irresistible lassitude. Athletes who wish to attain a high physical performance quickly, without burdening the digestion, take glucose. This enters the blood speedily and delivers fresh fuel to the muscles in the shortest possible time.

Long before any Olympic games ever took place or man had any idea of looking for the hidden strength to exploit it for his own ends, the hummingbirds were already living on this paragon of all energy foods. They obtained it from flowers whose nectar, like bee's honey, consists mainly of fructose and glucose. They require an incredible amount – more than half their body weight per day – even of a substance as rich as this in calories. For a human this would correspond to a daily intake of eighty to a hundred pounds of glucose, or calculated in other foods, to 140 pounds of bread or 280 pounds of veal or 380 pounds of potatoes. Apart from nectar, hummingbirds, like all warm-blooded animals, require protein, fats, minerals and vitamins. Each bird catches large numbers of small flies, spiders and other tiny creatures, and eats more than three hundred times a day in order to obtain sufficient quantity. It is indeed the life of a gourmand.

Refuelling in the air An endearing and romantic trait of these attractive creatures is that, like butterflies, they obtain their food from flowers. Hummingbirds and flowers are inseparable. These tiny birds are closely associated with flowers in that they remove the nectar from the flowers and provide a pollination service to them. Some have ornamental plumes, crests, trains and wimples of bizarre, orchid-like splendour and they even look like flowers.

They hover in front of blooms, dip their pointed bill like a probe into the calyx, work their forked tongue skilfully back and forth at high speed, hovering freely while sipping the drops of nectar. One stroke of the tail and they are in reverse, ready to go to the next flower. Often when the bill and tongue are not long enough to reach the base of the flower their head and neck disappear right into the calyx.

Some authors maintain that their sipping is comparable to the lapping of a cat; others see the tongue and bill as a kind of pumping mechanism, in which the liquid is sucked up by a vacuum produced by the tongue. I believe that the latter view is correct. How otherwise could a Sword-billed Hummingbird get the liquid up its four and half inch long bill which is as thin as a knitting-needle? The tongue works very fast. I estimate about ten pumping movements per second.

Sometimes the hummingbirds try to bore through the petals with the bill or push them apart from the side. In this they show considerable skill and aptitude.

Hummingbirds occur in the largest numbers and with the

greatest variety of species, in the vicinity of the equator where there are flowers in abundance throughout the whole year, flowering trees, shrubs, cacti and herbaceous plants in the forests, on the plains and also in gardens. Some species have favourite food flowers, others visit every plant including introduced garden plants, indeed every speck of colour is investigated for nectar.

Thus the Ruby-throated Hummingbird has been observed at no fewer than twenty-eight plant species, the Rufous Hummingbird at twenty-one. In Europe in captivity, they also try their luck at every flower. When a new bunch of flowers is put into the aviary they immediately fly over and examine it. They are able to adjust quickly to changes in the type of flower offered. They even pay attention to objects that only faintly resemble flowers.

My Blue-throated Sylph, *Aglaiocercus kingi*, which was allowed to fly free in my workroom, never made any attempt to escape. It showed no interest in the window but visited every spot of colour in the room, particularly anything that was red; this included pictures, spots on my tie, red knobs on the typewriter, and even my daughter's red lips. The little bird buzzed round her head like a bee and with true southern temperament tried to insert its bill between her lips. My daughter was relieved that it was not our Sword-billed Hummingbird, *Ensifera ensifera*, which took this liberty.

Plants visited by hummingbirds

The plants printed in italics are flowers, shrubs and trees that can be seen in European gardens.

Abutilon	*Canna*	Datura	*Gladiolus*
Aesculus	*Carduus*	Deloperone	*Godetia*
Agave	*Castilleja*	*Delphinium*	
Aloe	Cattleya	Dombeya	*Helianthus*
Althaea	Centro-		*Hibiscus*
Aquilegia	pogon	*Epilobium*	
Arcto-	Cereus	Erythrina	*Impatiens*
staphylos	Chilopsis	Eucalyptus	*Ipomoea*
Asclepias	Cirsium		*Iris*
	Citrus	Fouquiera	
Begonia	*Clematis*	*Fuchsia*	*Lantana*
Beloperone	Cleome		Larrea
Bouvadia	*Convolvulus*	*Gentiana*	*Lilium*
Buddleia	*Crataegus*	Gilia	*Lobelia*

67

Lonicera	Nerium	Portulaca	Syringa
Lupinus	Nicotiana	Primula	
Lycium		Prunus	Teconia
	Oenothera		Tropaeolum
Madia	Opuntia	Ramona	
Malvastrum		Ribes	Verbena
Marcgravia	Parkinsonia	Robinia	Vinca
Melia	Passiflora	Rodriguezia	
Mertensia	Pedicularis	Rosa	Yucca
Mimulus	Penstemon		
Mirabilis	Petunia	Salvia	Zauschneria
Monarda	Phaseolus	Sambucus	
	Phlox	Scrophularia	
Nepeta	Poinciana	Symphoricarpus	

Do hummingbirds sleep?

I was as pleased as Punch when I drove to the airport to fetch my first hummingbirds. It was night and I reported to the counter of the air-freight section punctually, to await the scheduled arrival of the Boeing from New York. I asked the assistant to make sure that the box with its valuable contents would be immediately unloaded and brought into a warm room without delay. As it turned out the aeroplane was late. I began to worry about the birds, especially about one species, the Velvet-purple Coronet, *Boissonneaua jardini*, which had never been brought to Europe before. Eventually the aeroplane was announced: 'Lufthansa flight 402 from New York has landed'. How would the tiny passengers from Colombia, Ecuador and Brazil have borne the flight?

My valuable box was unloaded promptly, and as it was handed over to me it was clear that my cargo of little birds had aroused more interest than anything else on the flight. I took a hasty look into the cloth-lined box, to make sure that the number tallied with that shown on my official form and then hurried home with my treasures.

Having brought them safely home, I opened the travelling cage expecting that one hummingbird after another would fly out, free at last. But there was no sign of any movement at all. I removed the cloth round the sides and there they were – five specimens, feathers ruffled, eyes closed, motionless, the bills raised up like thorns, crouching on the perch. They looked as though they were torpid

68

and did not even appear to be breathing. Were they asleep? I tapped the box, but they did not move. I tilted the cage, even turned it upside down and shook it. The birds were not alive. Like stuffed bodies nailed to the bar they allowed themselves to be turned around without moving or falling off. What had happened to them?

I touched them gently with my finger. They were stiff and felt cold to the touch. In dismay I carefully took hold of one and tried to pick it up. But I could not lift it off the perch because its feet, stiff and rigid like the rest of its body, would not release their grasp on the bar.

While I was still holding my hand round the lifeless body, wondering what to do next, something remarkable happened. Up till then there had been no trace of a heartbeat, but suddenly I could feel pulsating movement: the tiny bird started to breathe, slowly and faintly at first but in the course of five minutes the breathing became faster and deeper. After about ten minutes the bird began to move in my hand. It released its grip on the bar. When it opened its eyes and looked at me I offered it a feeding-bottle. Without any sign of fear it started to take short drinks, only a little at first and then long draughts. The bird visibly gained strength from minute to minute and when it began to tread and spread its wings actively I opened my hand and – brrr – it flew off.

In this way I brought one hummingbird after another back to life, and an hour later they were all in the air. How can one explain this remarkable phenomenon? The birds had been dispatched in the cool, dark freight compartment of the aeroplane. It is possible that any other bird would have suffered from inflammation of the lungs. A hummingbird, however, survives the dark and cold, together with an absence of food that entails a loss of internal and external heat, because it is able to reduce its metabolism by means of an obscure process that is not yet fully understood. Respiration and heartbeat are reduced. The body temperature, normally about forty degrees Centigrade, is lowered. The bird becomes torpid like a lizard in hibernation. In this way hummingbirds survive the cold and periods without food in a state of torpidity.

The extent to which its own temperature falls depends on the outside temperature and on the general state of health and nutrition of the individual animal. The lowest temperature measured was

69

eighteen degrees Centigrade. I noticed that new arrivals, which were in a weak state, took longer to come round than acclimatised birds, both being tested under the same external temperature conditions.

I have never seen them hanging upside down in a torpid condition as has sometimes been stated. It is, however, possible that a torpid hummingbird might capsize. They do not stick their head under the wings or lay it along the back, but the bill is held pointing into the air, sticking up like a thorn. This position may possibly be related to the condition of torpidity or it may have something to do with camouflage and concealment. The deeper a hummingbird sleeps the more erect is the bill held. If the night is warm the lethargy does not appear to be so deep. The bill is held at a less steep angle, the breathing is still perceptible and the bird awakes quickly.

As soon as twilight arrives they go to their roosting place without delay, and in an indoor aviary the half light can be simulated by switching off the lamps in stages. There is no more preening or play and they stop moving. They put their bills up and they are instantly fast asleep.

Icy cold and far out to sea One day in New York when the city was seized by icy winds, a garage attendant running over to his pumps saw a small object creeping along the wall and falling to the ground. He picked it up and examined it. It was a little Ruby-throated Hummingbird, cold and benumbed, as though dead. Fortunately, the man knew what to do: he laid the bird in a warm box and took it to the zoo. There the bird woke up after being warmed in the hands for a few minutes and flew around in the heated aviary with the other hummingbirds.

On the same day, an orange seller decided to move his fruit back into his shop because of the sudden cold. Groping amongst the oranges his hand touched something that felt like feathers. This turned out to be another Ruby-throat, one of the many which the zoo has to this day.

Once during the winter I took some hummingbirds to an exhibition. On the way the car heater failed. When I finally reached my destination the hummingbirds were laid out on the floor like so many frozen corpses. At that moment nobody would have given me twopence for my precious birds. All the other aviculturists who were busy putting up cages and aviaries looked at me in sympathy.

70

But I held the hummingbirds in my hands and breathed on them, and after a quarter of an hour they made it quite clear by their energetic trampling that they no longer required outside help and buzzed off. To the bystanders this looked like some kind of conjuring trick.

In the seventeenth century when Father Bernabe Cobo wanted to make his Indians understand the miracle of the resurrection, he quoted as evidence the awakening of hummingbirds. New light is shed on this mystery, however, when one learns that Chilean women awaken hummingbirds by warming them in their bosoms. This is what confronted the pious Father Cobo and he wrote about it in his book *Historia del Nuevo Mundo*.

I cannot say how long a cold and torpid hummingbird will live in this state since I was not willing to submit them to this kind of experiment. In any case the body uses its fuel reserves very sparingly when the metabolism is much reduced, and it can be safely said that the bird will certainly survive for two to three days. Hummingbirds are remarkably tough. I have seen sick specimens which have lingered on in a lethargic state for more than a week after they have stopped feeding.

When fully active, a hummingbird generally needs to 'fill up' every ten minutes. If it cannot find anything to feed on after two or three hours of energetic searching, it becomes less active and, apart from odd flights, it finally remains perched and begins to sleep.

Normally a hummingbird has no reserve of fuel, but what happens to a Ruby-throated Hummingbird that has to fly continuously for eight hours? Here too nature has a solution. Before its great flight – and only then – the bird is in a position to put on an incredibly large amount of fat which serves as transit fuel. This storage of fat adds more than fifty per cent to its normal body weight. By comparison, a man intending to give an eight hour performance as energetic as that of a hummingbird would have to deposit a layer of fat weighing eighty pounds, and live on this food reserve throughout that day.

We do not know the nature of the mechanism responsible for organising this unusual increase in weight. It is believed that certain hormones provide the stimulus but nobody knows which ones or in what way they function.

The breeding season

Hummingbirds are skilled construction engineers. Their nests are very inconspicuous – one has to search carefully and for a long time before discovering one – but they are beautiful and elaborate constructions. The choice of site and the stability of the structure are also remarkable. Sometimes the nest is suspended in such a way that it appears to defy the laws of gravity. Some of the nests are daring examples of constructional engineering. A Reed Warbler requires three or four stems as support for its nest but a hummingbird of the genus *Phaethornis* completes its architectural masterpiece by anchoring it firmly to a single, vertical unbranched stem or to the tip of a narrow leaf which hangs down. The small structure is attached only at one side and to prevent it from capsizing as the bird lands on it, the hummingbird weights the lower ends of the nesting material with little stones and pieces of earth.

How can a small bird which has only its slender bill as a tool manage to perform such tasks? Few other birds know how to plait and glue better than the hummingbird, which chooses the most suitable material with the greatest care. It uses spiders' webs, cottonwool or other plant fibres, down, moss, lichen, hair, feathers, thin grass stems, leaves and petals, thin twigs, and pieces of bark. Hummingbirds are selective and search with great pertinacity for the material that is habitual to the species. If they cannot come by the right kind of material honestly they do not hesitate to steal it, and under certain circumstances they will demolish unfamiliar nests completely.

At one time I had a Brown Inca of unknown sex. One day, however, this bird flew over to me as I entered the aviary and started to pull at my hair. Some people might have thought the bird was trying to play with me but this was not so. It was definitely my hair that attracted attention and it buzzed round me, pulling bits out of my head. It was obviously a female gathering nesting material. It would not leave me alone and rather than lose my fine crop of hair, I eventually took various bits of nesting material into the aviary hoping that this would put matters right. First I offered her some

Opposite:
An attractive scene. Flying ceaselessly to and fro they weave the finest nests out of moss, hempfibres and delicate grasses. Above: a female Blue-throated Sylph, *Aglaiocercus kingi*, builds a roofed structure, whereas the Rufoustailed Hummingbird, *Amazilia tzacatl* (below left) builds a deep funnel. Below right: the Brown Inca, *Coeligena wilsoni*, was the first hummingbird to lay in Europe; this female twice laid a couple of eggs which she incubated patiently and without any apparent fear.

72

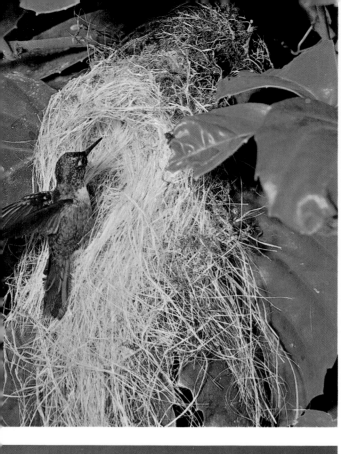

◁ Hummingbirds are also completely at home with cactus blooms. To me these birds are still mysterious, being often so difficult to identify. This one (above) on the flower of a Repsalis cactus, is possibly *Amazilia iodura*. Below: the beautiful *Boissonneaua flavescens* on an aloe.

It is but rarely that *Florisuga mellivora* fans out its tail feathers for a fraction of a second in such an attractive manner. It was only after about three hundred attempts that I was fortunate enough to obtain this enchanting shot of bird and flower together.

pposite:

he form of individual species of
ummingbird is very varied. The
/hite-lipped Sicklebill (top left) is
erfectly adapted for sucking nectar
om flowers. The Sword-billed
lummingbird, *Ensifera ensifera*, a
ale from Ecuador, (bottom right)
as the extreme form of 'pipeline'
hich is apparently designed for
owers with a deep calyx. In spite
f the length of the bill it man-
euvres just as skilfully as the
lack-throated Train-bearer, *Lesbia*
ctoriae, a male from Ecuador
ottom left) which has long
rnamental feathers that do not
pear to hinder its aerial acro-
atics. The Purple-crowned Fairy,
eliothryx barroti, (top right) from
razil, is one of the few humming-
rds with pure white in its
umage.

fine grasses which she ignored. I then tried her with moss and lichen but got the same negative response. She also rejected horsehair with seeming contempt. I ransacked the house, outhouses and garden to find spiders' webs. The amount I collected was so paltry that she either never found it in spite of searching eagerly or she regarded the supply as inadequate from the start. I even wondered if I should visit the barber and have my hair cut but desisted, hoping for some other way out of the dilemma. I finally offered her some extremely fine, clean, yellowish hemp fibres, which are used as tow in sail-making and engineering work. She accepted this material and also some cotton fibres.

There followed a series of enchanting events, each one making a charming vignette. First, the female carefully chose her nesting-place. She flew busily about the thickly over-grown aviary and constantly attacked other hummingbirds. She repeatedly lowered herself down onto certain forked branches, pressed her breast against them and gracefully spread her wings, as though she were already sitting on a nest or perhaps measuring the sites for size. She let herself glide from the branch, forwards and backwards a dozen times, repeatedly testing the take-off and landing from all directions. She then rejected this place and began the same performance at two other spots. Eventually she found a suitable branch two feet above the ground, in a site that was hidden under a roof of leaves. It was also conveniently placed from the photographic point of view.

Many people probably have watched hummingbirds in flight pulling off delicate fibres and chasing after cobwebs drifting in the wind; they catch them and then, still flying, build them into the nest. The threads which my Brown Inca took first were up to four inches long and she placed these crosswise on the branch. She picked up the loose ends and while still flying, sometimes also perching, she coiled them in a clockwise direction around the branch. In this way a small firmly interlocking ball of material that looked like an encrusted cushion gradually came into being. This was subsequently heightened and broadened.

The bird sometimes used its bill like a darning needle. Loose threads were stuck into the ball and drawn out at the side, as though properly stitched up into place. It flew round and round the structure, removing loose threads and tucking them into other places. Thus it smoothed off and rounded the whole structure.

77

When the cushion was large enough for the bird to lower herself on to it, she began working actively with her feet, twisting and turning round, and bending the edges of the cushion upwards with her bill and neck, thus making the structure into the shape of a flat saucer.

At this stage of nest-building, every time the bird took off some of the meshwork remained attached to her claws and she destroyed half of what she had just built. I decided to catch her and clip her claws although I was not sure how she would react.

After this interference she went on strike for three days, but I need not have worried: as I have already said, hummingbirds are thoroughly obstinate and on the fourth day she resumed work with redoubled energy and was busy the whole day long. She collected material, built it into the structure, weaving and shaping the nest and taking time in between for drinking, bathing, preening and driving off other hummingbirds in aggressive sorties. It was a stupendous performance for such a tiny bird.

The structure grew until, later, it was shaped like a hemisphere. Lying in the cup of the nest the bird now smoothed the edge carefully, using her neck, throat, bill and wings which were extended in a graceful movement that looked like an embrace. The outer wall of the nest received a final touch; she frequently used her tongue, sliding it quickly over protruding fibres until they lay flat.

After five straight days of construction, the masterpiece was finished except for the internal fittings and the decoration and camouflage of the outside. These were completed during short flights, after the eggs had already been laid.

The next female to build her nest in the aviary was a *Damophila julie*. She used the same materials but chose a place very high up, just under the roof. This hummingbird also built a hemispherical structure, but the cup was so deep that during incubation all one could see of the bird was its tail held stiffly erect.

An *Amazilia tzacatl*, infected by the outbreak of nest-building, produced a charming structure in the form of a deep cup. Anchorage was first obtained with hemp and cotton, but for the walls this bird preferred a stronger weave of horsehair which she later covered with bits of moss and lichen. *Chrysolampis mosquitus* used cotton almost exclusively, but employed her tongue more frequently than the other hummingbirds for smoothing and gluing.

78

Finally, after days of fruitless searching for a site and after some tentative experiments one of my Blue-throated Sylphs, *Aglaiocercus kingi*, began to build on a forked branch about twelve inches below the ceiling of the room. At first she worked like the Brown Inca, *Coeligena wilsoni*, and made a firmly interwoven cushion of hemp fibres on the branch; she raised the edges of the cushion, strengthened them with moss and then smoothed them down. When the nest took on the shape of a bowl, I thought the structure was finished and would be left in this rough state. To my astonishment, however, she then started to raise the edges of the nest, leaving a narrow recess at the front as a landing place. Skilfully drawing the material up over her head, she gradually made first an arch and then a complete roof. Working always from the inside she strengthened and lined it. The finished product was almost completely enclosed except for a small entrance hole.

Nests of hummingbirds show a wide variety of shapes. In addition to bowls and cups there are some that look like small nut-shells. *Lampornis clemenciae* builds an elongate, loose pouch, attractively decorated with festoons of grass. The most daring constructions of all are those that are suspended from only two points of attachment and swing freely like hammocks. Cobwebs that are sticky and elastic – and thus resistant – are indispensable for these works of art.

My friend Don Martino Springer, Professor of Architecture, wrote to me from Chile: 'On three occasions I have had the good fortune to be able to see nest-building taking place on an ivy-clad wall, barely three yards from my office window. The artistically woven nest was attached to a branch and consisted of moss, lichen and wool – sometimes a few threads were also used – and all the delicate material was found by the hummingbirds in the neighbourhood.'

'Owing to the type of material used the structure appears quite inconspicuous. Some of our present-day avant-garde architects could well profit by this example of art at its best, achieved by the greatest simplicity and not by orgies of form and colour!'

Model husband or Don Juan It is not only the good and beautiful aspects of hummingbirds that must be mentioned in this book. It is well known that all that glitters is not gold, and beauty of form is not always indicative of a gentle spirit. Take the male hummingbird for example. Like the

79

brave and dashing knights of the Middle Ages, their brilliant plumage flashes like shining armour and they woo the females with a boldness that brooks no denial. They take their females by storm. No sooner than discovered, the bewildered female is overwhelmed by a display of fireworks, of light and colour, daring aerobatics, vibrating wings and chirping song. More intimidated than enamoured and more by shock than persuasion she submits to her tempestuous wooer.

A tiny male *Damophila* sat singing and beating its wings like a star performer beside its mate. But each time he reached the peak of his display she flew off. He followed her angrily, increased his humming to miniature thunderclaps, caught up with her in flight and with his bill at her tail, they circled several times around the aviary and then they went down on to a leaf – she half drawing him down and he sinking on to her – where they mated without further formalities.

Such boldness on the part of the impudent lover would be excusable if he were prepared to abide by the consequences, but the male hummingbird does not settle down with one female. Far from being the faithful type he not only tries his luck with other females of his own species, but also with those of other species and many hybrids have been recorded.

The female does not always capitulate quickly and unconditionally. My Blue-tailed Emerald, *Chlorostilbon mellisugus*, worked for weeks to impress his chosen one. He was a crazy little devil, highly excitable, and he buzzed back and forth – wings vibrating loudly and chirping breathlessly – only half an inch from the tip of her bill as she sat on a branch. She followed his rapid movements with her head, so that both bills pointed at each other like needles. But before he dared to take the decisive step she always shot away from him with an angry whiz and beat him in flight. Although he persisted in his attentions, these two never paired.

On the other hand I once saw a female formally presenting herself. When my female *Coeligena wilsoni* had finished nest-building and had still not secured a mate, she took a piece of cottonwool in her bill and danced up and down in front of a male *Heliodoxa rubinoides*, which is about the same size and also brownish in colour. She performed an attractive and enchanting courtship flight but he was clearly not aware of being accosted.

80

Following the brief courtship ceremonies of the hummingbirds, the female remains alone after mating. She has no time to languish over the unfaithful Casanova. She finishes building the nest on her own and also incubates and rears the young alone. There appear to be a few laudable exceptions. Thus the male of the Sparkling Violet-ear, *Colibri coruscans*, has been seen to incubate. Also males of some other species have been observed for long periods on or in the vicinity of the nest.

It is possible that at one time necessity may have driven the males into leading such sharply separate and solitary lives. By this I mean that the daily task of obtaining vast amounts of food may have caused them to become such marked individualists and egoists.

Two-chick system The reader already has had to endure so many superlatives about hummingbirds that I shall doubtless be regarded as the biggest exaggerator of all natural history writers. Nevertheless, I must now state that in proportion to their body weight hummingbirds lay the largest eggs of any bird.

There is no doubt about this. Geroudet (1954) writes: 'The hummingbird *Lampornis clemenciae* is only half as heavy as a Marsh Tit, but it lays eggs that are approximately the same size.' Aviculturists who have visited me and passed an opinion on the clutch of *Coeligena wilsoni* were surprised to see that the eggs of this bird were approximately as large as those of a Cordon-bleu which is twice as heavy. The performance of this feat is not easy for the female *Coeligena*. Some entries in my notebook indicate the extent of her exertions.

21 JULY 1964

0530 hrs Early in the morning I took up my position twenty-five inches in front of the nest in order to take more photographs of the bird at its nest-building.

0600 hrs The bird is no longer building. It flies around in the aviary, restless and noticeably aimless. For minutes at a time it remains sitting on its usual perch, a twig in the vicinity of the nest. It ruffles its feathers, looks ill and breathes faster than usual.

0610 hrs The bird flies to the nest.

0612 hrs Very restless on the nest. It spends more time standing than sitting. It also turns round in circles and patters about in the nest.

81

0613 hrs It begins to push, or bear down, at irregular intervals, roughly every ten to fifteen seconds. Each time the feathers are ruffled up. The bill is directed obliquely upwards.

0615 hrs The pushing is now repeated regularly at five second intervals. Between the intervals it turns round in circles and treads alternately with its feet. Sometimes the bird presses its vent against the inner edge of the nest, with the tail-feathers spread out and vibrating.

0625 hrs The 'labour pains' now occur at regular intervals of one second. At each push the female lifts herself up rather high. A tiny bit of the egg, about the size of a pinhead, is seen briefly but it slips back again. The pushing appears to tax the bird's strength. Each time it emits a weak piping sound. Other hummingbirds become interested and fly round the nest inquisitively.

0629 hrs More of the egg is visible, amounting to about the size of a pea, but it still continues to slip back again.

0632 hrs The bird is now positioned so that the vent is aimed at the centre of the nest. Its head and breast project so far over the edge of the nest that I am afraid that the bird may lose its balance and fall out.

0635 hrs With one final big effort the female ejects the egg. It slides exactly into the centre of the nest bowl. The bird remains standing, breathing fast for about ten seconds; it then continues standing motionless above the egg.

0636 hrs It lowers itself and rests for ten minutes with eyes closed.

0647 hrs The bird flies to a feeding-bottle and drinks copiously of the liquid food. Returns to the nest, perches briefly on the edge, touches the egg with its bill, lowers itself into the nest and rests.

0655 hrs Flies off, drinks food solution and then pure water. Chases other hummingbirds which approach its nest.

0700 hrs Greater activity once again. Drinking, flying, defending the nest and, in between, a few minutes on the nest. The egg is touched from the edge of the nest with the bill but not turned. Sometimes it flies to the nest, peers in while hovering and then looks for a perch.

0715 hrs Bathing, preening.

On this and the following day the bird did not incubate. It visited the nest every three to four hours and lowered itself down for no longer than a few minutes. But it made violent attacks on every

82

other hummingbird that approached the nest. On the third day the bird laid its second egg. This time it was achieved with less trouble.

23 JULY 1964

0740 hrs The bird is flying around restlessly and aimlessly. Other hummingbirds, even an *Amazilia*, which steal its nest material do not upset it.

0754 hrs Flies to the nest. Behaves quietly. Plumage ruffled.

0812 hrs Begins to push and turn round in the nest.

0823 hrs Rhythmical pushing every two to three seconds.

0828 hrs The second egg is laid. The bird rests.

0836 hrs The bird feeds.

0905 hrs The bird is once again completely active: drinks, flies, fights, preens and bathes, patrols its nest.

At 0943 hours on the same day the hummingbird sat imperturbably on its eggs. I could do what I liked in the aviary. It was not disturbed by the daily routine of cleaning up which went on all round it and even allowed the fine spray of water to pass over it. It reacted to the electronic flash with no more than a flicker of the eye. It even allowed me to touch it.

It flew off only to feed or to search for more nesting material, repairing the nest, camouflaging it and raising the edge. When it took off it either floated gently up or rose impetuously without perceptible preparation. This also applied to its landings. Sometimes the bird remained in flight in the vicinity of the nest, looking around in various directions and then suddenly scurried into the nest like a mouse. At other times it lost height slowly and gently, descending like a parachute onto the eggs. It only perched on the edge of the nest when it was engaged in building operations. The eggs were turned with the feet, not with the bill.

On the average the female came off the nest once in every thirty-nine minutes. The longest daily spell of incubation without any interruption – excluding the nights – was one hour and sixteen minutes; the shortest was twenty minutes. With reduced activity the frequency of feeding also dropped. As in all other hummingbirds the eggs were pure white like porcelain. Each clutch contains only two eggs. There are scarcely any exceptions to this. Bearing in mind all the effort that the tiny creature has to expend in the process of egg-laying one has to admit that this clutch size seems quite large enough.

83

The following are a few examples of egg sizes (1 mm = 0·04 inch):

Coeligena wilsoni	14 × 9	mm
Selasphorus rufus	13 × 8·5	mm
Hylocharis leucotis	13 × 8	mm
Mellisuga minima	12 × 8	mm
Damophila julie	9 × 6	mm

Most species, particularly those in northern and central America, breed twice a year. The Brown Inca, *Coeligena wilsoni*, which was flown to me in Europe from Costa Rica, did not alter its inborn habits and produced two clutches in that year.

So far it has not been possible to establish precise breeding data for hummingbirds in tropical regions. However, two clutches are probably the minimum. When breeding is unsuccessful the bird may try a third and perhaps even a fourth time, provided that the pair still remain in full breeding condition.

The individual species of hummingbird incubate for different periods. The incubation period varies from twelve to twenty-nine days. Differences in climate may be significant but there is still a great deal that needs investigation in this field.

After fourteen days of uninterrupted incubation my *Coeligena wilsoni* became restless, flew off, danced around the nest and touched the eggs repeatedly with her bill. She then incubated for a half hour longer, left the nest again and went to her usual perch. She checked the eggs several times. On the following day, the fifteenth, she often examined the eggs by looking at them and gently touching them with her bill. Finally she pecked at them gingerly. They were empty. This was inevitable as they were infertile, no male having been present during the breeding season.

When the bird saw that no chicks could be expected she covered the eggs with cottonwool, flew off, bathed and then took no further interest in them. Five days later, however, she invited another hummingbird to mate by dancing up and down in front of it with nest material in her bill. On the sixth day after the end of the first abortive incubation, she began to rebuild her old nest. Then one day she laid an egg and two days later a second one. In this way the female completed her second clutch. This time she went on incubating the eggs for twenty-three days, conscientiously and courageously, if not without a certain bewilderment during the final days. Then once more she pecked at the infertile eggs and that was the end of her second attempt. I cannot help admiring the way this female never showed any sign of disappointment over her two unsuccessful attempts. She was and is to this day a gay and carefree virgin.

Unfortunately I have still not been able to observe a hummingbird feeding its young. It must be a remarkable sight, as the female inserts her long bill into the gapes of the young, an experience which they presumably find both alarming as well as enjoyable. Imagine this procedure in the Sword-billed Hummingbird! Who would like to use a knitting-needle to feed his children with? Or, bearing in mind comparative size, who would insert a six-foot long beanstalk into the throat of a baby? The tip of the bill must be very sensitive if the food is to be passed to the young without injuring them.

After observing the accuracy with which the Sword-billed Hummingbird can hit the centre point of the smallest flower, I believe that it can use its 'pipeline' with just as much precision for pumping the liquid out. As in all nidicolous, or nest-reared birds, hummingbird nestlings are born naked; they are only the size of a bee and some are even smaller. Their bills are relatively short and grow in the course of time. At first the female feeds her young from the edge of the nest, but later on she feeds them while still in flight. The young birds fledge after two to three weeks; they then leave the nest and do not return. The female continues to feed them while in flight for a few more days and thereafter they find their own food.

Although only one-sixth to one-third of all broods are reared successfully, a benign providence ensures that large numbers of these attractive creatures survive – in spite of the two–chick system.

Hummingbirds
and man

A male Blue-throated Sylph,
Aglaiocercus kingi (Venezuela).
With movements as fast as a flick
of an eyelid one has to release the
shutter in advance if one is to
capture the bird in all its beauty.

Above: Among the
smallest; the Rufous
Hummingbird, *Selasphorus
rufus* from California (top
left) migrates a distance of
about 1900 miles. On the
right, a pair of White-
bellied Woodstars,
Acestrura mulsanti, from
Ecuador, on a Cattleya
flower. Below: The
Velvet-purple Coronet,
Boissonneaua jardini (a male
from Ecuador), one of the
most fabulously beautiful
species. Its plumage
sparkles like jewels.

bove:
amophila julie, a
ale on fuchsia.
elow: the flight
f a Blue-
roated Sylph is
ntrancing
hether the bird
flying fast or
iding gently.

In South America

There are idealists and materialists among human beings. Some time ago I had a guest from South America who belonged to the second category. I classified him without any hesitation amongst the materialists after he had remarked: 'Hummingbirds are charming little birds but when they're plucked there is not much left on them.'

This is not the kind of aviculture I have in mind when I speak of the love that the Americans have for these small creatures. Whether they live in the northern, southern or central parts of their continent the majority of them are idealists and have always enjoyed the beauty, the charm and the individuality of hummingbirds without, at the same time, wanting to eat them.

Regarding the attitude of the people of Costa Rica, my young friend Michael Stedem reports from San José: 'The inhabitants of Costa Rica are of course no longer pure-blooded Indians but they still maintain some of the native superstitions and firmly believe that hummingbirds and their nests bring luck. The nests of the smallest and most colourful hummingbird of Costa Rica, the *rey de los gorriones*, are in particular demand. They will risk their lives by climbing to the top of the tallest trees to fetch these enchanting nests, structures that are hardly bigger than a walnut and are popularly known as *macua*. The Costa Ricans clean the small nests, put perfume on them, and then carry them on their belts or hang them as talismans in their motor cars.'

Apart from the magic spell that is ascribed to hummingbirds by superstition, everyone is delighted when these birds build their nests on or in their houses. They regard these attractive visitors as bearers of good luck, just as Europeans do swallows. Innumerable people on the American continent attract them to their gardens and try to hold them there by cultivating plants with flowers particularly favoured by hummingbirds. They hang little bottles of sugar and honey solution in the window in order to be able to watch them at close range or to enjoy their unusual flight with its bewitching play

Opposite:
Damophila julie, a male on *Columnea* (much enlarged). In spite of its tiny size – weight only three grams – this dwarf bird will fearlessly attack other hummingbirds over the rights to a flower. When this happens the loud hum of the rapidly vibrating wings rises to a crescendo of miniature thunder-claps. In fact the wings of a hummingbird can only be seen as a shadow. It was not until the advent of the electronic flash that the movement could be frozen.

93

of colour. I myself cannot say whether hummingbirds really bring luck, but they certainly stir the imagination. All the beauty that we love and admire in birds is heightened in them. You may consider yourself lucky when you see them, just as you may consider it a red-letter day when you see an orchid or a rare butterfly.

Eucalyptus trees and honey-pots

Man usually only has to see something to be overcome by a desire to possess it. He likes to pursue something that eludes him, and once it is safely captured, he wants to hold on to it: jewels and precious metals, beetles, flowers and butterflies, and birds of many kinds are kept by various people all over the world. Attempts at keeping hummingbirds in captivity have not been lacking. For almost a century zoological gardens have been trying to keep these flying jewels in cages and aviaries with varying degrees of success.

It was in America that hummingbirds were first kept in captivity. Transport problems do not play a major role and there are sufficient opportunities for bird-catchers to exercise their skill. Professional ornithologists were the first to try their hand at keeping these birds in captivity but private research workers and aviculturists also devoted themselves to the problem. Thus, C.H. Greenewalt records that a Frenchman, Dr Etienne Beraut, kept more than twenty species on the twelfth floor of a block of flats in Rio de Janeiro. Unfortunately these birds, which Greenewalt would have been delighted to see and photograph, all died prematurely from a peculiar fungal infection. (With the help of the Munich University Animal Clinic I have been able to establish that this disease is due to an infection by a fungus of the candida group. Successful treatment is possible with moronal.)

In the *National Geographic Magazine* for January 1963, Mr Luis Marden writes of Dr Augusto Ruschi as a naturalist who 'understands the language of hummingbirds'.

Dr Ruschi was born in Santa Teresa, a small town in the Brazilian state of Espirito Santo. At first his passion, like that of his father and grandfather who had emigrated from the South Tyrol, was for the thousands of different species of bromeliad and orchid which occur in Brazil. He observed how some of those that grow on the trees as epiphytic plants come into bloom with a resounding bang. He tracked them down by their strong scent and observed the way in which they were pollinated. While doing this he became more and

94

more fascinated by the general behaviour of the hummingbirds, which buzzed around the flowers, dipped their bills and heads into the calyx and reappeared covered in pollen.

Dr Ruschi keeps his hummingbirds, most of which he has caught himself, in aviaries that are huge by European standards. The largest is one hundred and fifty feet long, forty-five feet broad and eighteen feet high. Here the birds live completely free as though in the wild. The warm sun shines on a forest of flowering trees and shrubs, eucalyptus and hibiscus; the park shimmers with green, gold and red, and is filled with the humming of the birds.

He supplements the natural food supply of nectar by offering his birds a sugary solution in small bottles, which the birds sip greedily, and masses of fruitflies which he attracts by putting out plenty of rotting fruit. Thus the birds live under completely natural conditions. The air outside the aviaries in Santa Teresa also swarms with hummingbirds. Many eucalyptus trees, planted by Dr Ruschi and his forefathers, grow in this park. Sometimes one can see over a hundred hummingbirds on a single tree, representing as many as fourteen different species.

They also fly about the terrace of the old house. Thirty-two species fly to the feeding-bottles throughout the year, so that as one sits out of doors in the twilight, the air appears to be vibrating. When the eucalyptus trees are in full bloom the birds are less attracted to the sugary liquid. They prefer to feed on the flower nectar.

In 1957 Dr Ruschi paid a visit to the British Museum (Natural History) with Dr Jacques Berlioz, the French ornithologist, to examine the museum's fine collection of skins. Amongst them they looked at some fourteen skins of the species *Augastes lumachellus*. To their surprise they found that none of this species had been caught during the last half century. An argument developed. Dr Berlioz maintained that the species was extinct but Dr Ruschi suggested more cautiously: 'Brazil is a country the size of a continent, with more animals and plants in its rain-forests than in any other part of the world, with more than 20,000 species of moths and butterflies alone; an animal could remain concealed here for decades, without anybody seeing it. Why should a hummingbird species also not remain hidden in the secluded darkness of the forests for a long time?'

95

Dr Ruschi received from the museum two skins of the 'extinct' species as a pattern and decided to look for the living birds. First it was essential to find out where the last living specimens had been caught. The British Museum had been forced to make do with labelling specimens in terms of general geographical areas, such as Brazil, and detailed records regarding locality were not available. In the American Museum of Natural History in New York City, however, Dr Ruschi found a stuffed specimen with the more precise locality – Morro do Chapeu, Brazil. There are three towns with this name in Brazil. One of them lies at the foot of a mountain with the same name. Dr Ruschi decided to go there.

He flew to Bahia and covered the remainder of the journey by road. He left the pilot of a charter aeroplane waiting at the airfield with instructions to follow by air should he receive a cable from Dr Ruschi reporting success. The birds were to be brought out of the bush as quickly as possible and at all costs alive.

After eight days in the rain-forest Dr Ruschi had to admit defeat. He had found nothing, not even a feather. He cabled the pilot reporting failure and called off the expedition. He himself remained behind in order to photograph some remarkable geological formations in the mountains. At one waterfall, the Chacoeira do Ferro Doido, a chasm nearly six hundred feet deep had been eroded, revealing the rock strata. Cliffs with their colours and varied formations were a subject which also fascinated him and he stood quite still for a while, completely absorbed by the sight of the rocks.

All at once something flashed across his field of vision, a sparkling iridescence of green and gold in the air, and there was a familiar hum of wings – a hummingbird, but it was a species he had never before seen alive. Electrified he went in pursuit. Soon he saw it hovering in front of a yellow flower. There was no doubt at all: *Augastes lumachellus*. Overjoyed Ruschi telegraphed as soon as he could: 'Give me another forty-eight hours and I will bring it out to you.' After two days he had caught twenty-four males and females of the 'extinct' species and had succeeded in bringing them out safely. This created a minor scientific sensation. Later Dr Ruschi also discovered a hitherto unknown subspecies. He named it after his friend: *Colibri delphinae greenewalti*.

In Europe

The people of Europe are irresistibly attracted to the warmth of the Brazilian sunshine and the splendours of tropical profusion with their suggestion of glittering wealth. On 25 November 1905 a minute bird, symbolic of tropical splendour, landed in England: a *Colibri coruscans*, the beautiful iridescent blue, green and violet Sparkling Violet-ear. It was taken to the Zoological Gardens in London. From that day on the numbers of visitors rose by leaps and bounds. But in spite of all the care and effort taken in looking after this valuable bird it died after fourteen days. At that time nobody knew how to feed it.

In the years 1928 to 1931 other species arrived in London, Berlin and Leipzig. A few days after the arrival of the first consignment at Leipzig I happened to be, as I am so often, in the zoo. Little did I know what awaited me. I suddenly noticed that many of the visitors were streaming over to a small pavilion in the remoter part of the extensive gardens and clustering around the entrance. Two keepers were apparently having trouble controlling the stream of people and were trying to keep them on the move.

I joined the throng and, propelled rather than walking of my own free will, I finally succeeded in getting through the door. Inside I could see nothing but people packed like sardines, and the uniform caps of three extra keepers who were urging everyone to keep moving. The public gangway was in darkness; the only light came from some glass panes, which looked like aquaria. I recognised plants and flowers behind the glass and all of a sudden there was such an enchanting whirring and hovering, sparkling and glittering, that I have never forgotten that moment.

There were excited cries of astonishment; but, above the chatter, there was a humming of invisible wings and a thin twittering at intervals, clearly audible through the glass panes. The people read the word 'Kolibris' which was printed on a label attached to the glass pane and kept repeating it out loud to each other but they did not know what to make of this term. They argued amongst

97

themselves and started guessing – beetles, dragonflies or butterflies – until one man tried to explain with more or less authenticity that these were birds which had never before been seen in Europe.

The excitement reached its peak when suddenly – I do not know how it escaped – a hummingbird shot across the room. Hurriedly the doors of the pavilion were closed and people started to chase the bird. It was all very dramatic but neither the skill of the keepers nor the efforts of the shut-in spectators achieved anything. In the end it was the bird that solved the problem. After an hour it renounced its freedom and voluntarily flew back to the security of its cage and bottle, more or less safe and sound.

The technique of keeping these birds in zoos remained a problem and for many years the attempt had to be given up on account of excessive losses. The great drawing power of these very pretty creatures is shown by the case of the Englishman who saw them for the first time in the Copenhagen Zoo in 1935. He was so impressed that he cancelled a business flight which was already firmly booked in order to spend a few days quietly observing and studying these birds.

Difficulties of overseas transport It is not easy to bring live hummingbirds over to Europe from South America. It seems that the best method is the old one of going by sea. The most beautiful birds in the best physical condition have been brought personally by sea to a few Danes, Englishmen and Germans, by clever, experienced men such as Charles Cordier who caught and acclimatised the birds himself.

Such people took a lot of trouble with them during the voyage, checking on the correct temperature, and providing sufficient food and proper hygiene. As a result there were scarcely any losses, even when the voyage lasted a fortnight or three weeks. The catchers also removed sick or weakly birds before departure and released them into the wild. The great danger of disease spreading in the narrow confines of the travelling cage was thereby largely avoided.

Today, in our commercially ridden world we are forced to make use of general overseas exporters who handle motley consignments with varying degrees of care. It is true that the journey by air undoubtedly brings the birds over at great speed, but an aeroplane staff have neither the time nor the experience to take any interest in such small, even if valuable, freight.

98

All too often the light travelling cage is knocked about or turned over and damaged so that the honey solution pours out over the birds. They may be left in cold or draughty places where sudden drops in temperature may occur. All in all, they receive the kind of treatment that even an elephant could certainly not survive without illness. The main interest of the exporters and air companies is to fulfil the contract to deliver the birds alive. In every case this is achieved thanks to the short duration of the flight. But the only person who can testify as to whether they have arrived 'alive' or not is the recipient and, as they arrive mainly in the evening, he is forced to spend the night tending the birds single-handed. Smeared with honey and stiff with cold, the exhausted birds must be bathed and cleaned, dried and warmed and then fed by hand. In this way they are brought back to life.

It must be admitted that in recent years conditions have improved. Lately, I received consignments of beautiful specimens that were carefully packed and protected against draughts, and which arrived in good condition. The air lines have recently gone to a great deal of trouble to make plans for the future which will give these valuable birds every chance of arriving undamaged.

One scheme for solving the difficulties involved in transit was worked out with the help of the hummingbirds themselves, by making use of their unique capacity to withstand cold and the absence of food for a certain period by remaining in a torpid condition resembling hibernation. The scheme would appear to be quite straightforward: they are cooled down slowly so that they stop drinking and flying and become torpid; they are then put into small boxes like sardines and dispatched, finally being thawed out on arrival at their destination. What could be simpler? But although the theory was good it did not work in practice.

Various problems arise: for instance in the tropical heat of Brazil, to what temperature should they be reduced? To be pushed into a refrigerator, like a batch of carcasses, would not suit hummingbirds.

During the journey there is no guarantee that the temperature will remain at a steady low level. In the event that the birds begin to warm up on the way, they would wake up, start to move around and flutter, thus using up their reserves of energy before reaching their destination.

There is really no alternative but to put them into cages with a supply of food while they are still in an active condition. One can then only rely on the air lines to treat them with care and trust in providence. The shipper can telegraph or telephone the consignee of the time of arrival so that he can be ready to receive them at the airport with a heated car. The air freight people are only too willing to unload the birds immediately the aeroplane has landed and to bring them straight into the warmth.

Having made certain that they are all alive one can then acknowledge receipt. As soon as they are in the heated car, any of the birds that are in a weak condition should be warmed by holding them in the hand and given a drink (only the tip of the bill should be dipped in, so that no liquid can enter the respiratory organs). When they have regained the power of flight, the feeding-bottles are removed from the cage to prevent them being shaken during the car journey.

On arriving at home, birds with dirty plumage or with feathers stuck together with honey are bathed in a saucer of lukewarm water. They can be cleaned quickly with a wad of cottonwool. When all the cleaning and drying is done one is often astonished at the sight of an unexpectedly beautiful specimen sitting on the perch. As soon as they have recovered and are strong enough to stand up to the struggle for existence they are released into the communal aviary.

It is always a joy to see how quickly they regain their sparkling vitality. The private aviculturist will naturally not obtain his hummingbirds from overseas. If he buys them from an importer or dealer in his own country he can obtain birds that are already acclimatised and thus avoid a great deal of trouble.

Settling down in a dressing-gown

A catcher may have to wait a long time before he gets his first sight of the bird he is looking for. A great deal more time may elapse before he succeeds in catching it. I had to wait over four years before I was able to get even a single Sword-billed Hummingbird, and this specimen was probably the first ever to reach Germany alive.

When the precious rarity is actually in his hands, however, his troubles are not over and he still has to bring it out unharmed to civilisation. It is one thing to fly or transport a bird from one custodian to another, from exporter to importer, and from the latter to a zoo or aviculturist, in other words to send it on its way through civilised parts of the world. It is quite another matter to get it from the god-forsaken heights, perhaps fifteen thousand feet up in the Andes, down into the valley; the torrid bush where there are no paths must be negotiated before reaching any form of track, and then a vehicle must jolt its way over bumpy surfaces.

A hummingbird-catcher cannot be burdened with cages and glass-boxes when on the job. Neither can he carry home a wild-caught hummingbird in his bare hands. There is nothing to get a grip on: the bird is fragile and may be crushed like a butterfly or it can easily slip out of his hands between the index and middle finger even when the hand is closed. More subtle methods of transport are necessary for dealing with hummingbirds.

I do not know who first thought of the ingenious device of putting newly caught birds into the equivalent of a dressing-gown; it may have been Dr Ruschi or some Indian before him. To prevent a newly caught bird from damaging its head and plumage in a cage it is only necessary to immobilise its wings. A bit of cloth is drawn over it, like a kind of nightshirt. The cloth has a hole in the centre for the head, the shirt is pulled down smoothly and fastened below, enclosing the wings and the legs. The bird is then offered a feeding-bottle which it takes immediately like a baby. It is placed in a small box or put straight into one's pocket. It is amazing how calmly it behaves, lying quietly and not struggling to get free, just waiting to be fed again.

It is possible to dispatch a bird for short distances by car or in a coat pocket in this manner. One must not forget, however, to tie the tapes of the cloth carefully but firmly.

Which species to keep When I first developed a passion for hummingbirds and fell for the idea of keeping some of them myself, I was sufficiently naive to ask a South American exporter to send me a few of the most beautiful and rarest specimens. Among others on my list were the Crimson Topaz and the Frilled Coquette.

This first effort was received in stony silence. I next tried my luck with two other dealers. After a year of waiting for birds that never arrived and with empty cages on my hands, I was advised that there was a strict prohibition against catching and exporting humming-birds in several South American countries, including Brazil. In addition, I discovered that a beauty such as *Topaza pella* was very rare, difficult to find and still more difficult to catch. One can scarcely expect rarities to fall into his lap.

Finally I found a German importer who had good contacts in those countries which allowed the export of hummingbirds and who had access to several wonderful species. Even then I had to be patient because it was the rainy season in the areas concerned and so the catching was held up.

At last they arrived. Foremost were the attractive *Amazilia* species, *A. tzacatl* and *A. franciae*, one with a handsome iridescent green breast and brown fantail, the other with a metallic green head and white belly. These species are common and not too expensive. They might almost be described as the sparrows of the humming-bird world if such a comparison did not sound so disrespectful. Then there was a remarkably beautiful, medium-sized bird which appeared to be studded with hundreds of blue, green and violet spots – the Sparkling Violet-ear, *Colibri coruscans*. As its popular name suggests, the ear tufts, which can be erected in display when the bird is angry or excited, are characteristic. This species also is not particularly rare or expensive. The males and females of the Sparkling Violet-ear and of the *Amazilia* species have the same plumage and can scarcely be distinguished.

Another hummingbird that is not too rare is *Lesbia victoriae*, which has long tail feathers. It makes a marvellous picture with its widely forked and fan-like tail-feathers when turning sharply or doing fast manoeuvres in the air. The males have a pale iridescent emerald-green throat patch. In the female the very long train and the brilliant iridescence on the throat are lacking. But this, too, is an enchanting little bird with its shape and the delicate golden irides-cence of the feathers on its back.

The Blue-tailed Emerald, *Chlorostilbon mellisugus*, also is import-ed quite commonly; this is a tiny, compact, fast and impetuous bird of incredible vitality. In a good light it scintillates golden-green, sparkling like a brilliant display of fireworks.

A little larger, but more slender and graceful in all its movements, is *Hylocharis leucotis*, with variously coloured iridescent parts to the plumage that show golden, green, violet and topaz tones, and a faint suggestion of pink quartz in places.

A typically brilliant hummingbird is *Damophila julie*, tiny and glittering like a diamond, with green, blue and violet in its plumage. This species is fairly often on offer. Another available hummingbird, if one is lucky, is the Blue-throated Sylph, *Aglaio-cercus kingi*, an extremely elegant creature which is very lively and dashing in flight, but shows no sign of shyness towards humans. Although dotted with gold, it also shows off a green crest which glitters like a jewel, a cobalt-blue throat and two long, handsome blue-green tail-feathers.

One rarely sees the tiny North American Ruby-throated Hummingbird, *Archilochus colubris*, and the Rufous Hummingbird, *Selasphorus rufus*, as the capture and export of hummingbirds is also prohibited in the United States of America. Members of these species weigh only about two to two and a half grams. The males have the familiar ruby-red patch on the throat. One can only count on obtaining these species when they are caught fortuitously in their winter quarters in Central America. It appears to be difficult to get hold of these hornet-like aeronauts. In three years I have been able to buy only a single female of the *Selasphorus* species, a golden-brown bird with attractive white, black and red tail-feathers which are fanned out in flight. Some of the other forms that are not much larger than a bumblebee – such as species of *Acestrura*, *Calothorax*, and the smallest bird in the world, *Calypte helenae* (from Cuba) – rarely turn up in consignments.

Rarities of fabulous beauty, which must be regarded as outstanding even among hummingbirds, are the Ruby-topaz Hummingbird, *Chrysolampis mosquitus*, with deep red crown and shining golden breast and throat and the Velvet-purple Coronet, *Boisson-neaua jardini*, a species which has so far been brought to Europe alive only once. The latter appears to be studded all over with high-carat jewels, resembling cut diamonds, sapphires, emeralds, zircons and lapis-lazuli. When I saw it for the first time in bright light I was dazzled by so much beauty. The Sword-billed Hummingbird creates a sensation all its own. It is only the length of a man's finger and has a bill that looks like a knitting needle. When watching this bird as it manoeuvres in the air and among the flowers, or while it is preening and bathing, one wonders how it manages it all. My children regard it as a first-class show.

Whatever the particular contents of any consignment, it never fails to give pleasure. The commoner species are naturally cheaper;

they possess the typical characteristics of hummingbirds and in this way are not inferior by comparison with the rare and costly species. The amateur aviculturist is therefore well advised to try his luck first with the commoner species. There is no sense in insisting upon a particular species.

Hummingbirds are often given imaginary names by dealers. When one is offered, for example, a Cayenne Wood Hummingbird and a Fork-tailed Wood-nymph one assumes that these are different species. If these are ordered, it may well turn out that in fact they are a pair of one and the same species. A bird listed as a White-ear may well be a female Blue-tailed Emerald and so on. The only reliable name is the scientific one. It is for this reason that I generally use the Latin names. I do not blame the dealers and importers for using popular names, which are English or South American Indian in origin, as they have neither a complete zoological collection available for reference nor the six volumes of Gould's monograph which is extremely expensive. The nameless orphan must be given some kind of name which will serve as a guide to its identity. As far as the hummingbird is concerned, one name is as good as another and, to the amateur, the bird's name will not affect his enjoyment of it.

Aeronauts in showcases, indoor aviary and living-room

Neither Lora's parrot cage nor Hansi's golden castle were suitable abodes for a hummingbird. It would have flown in and out without the door being opened. A hummingbird feels at its best within four, smooth plain walls. A rectangular container forty-eight inches broad, thirty inches high and fifteen inches deep is an adequate size for two or three hummingbirds. If constructed of wood that matches the rest of the room, it will fit into the house as just another piece of furniture. The front should be made of window glass with two panes side by side, which slide in grooves. If the upper groove is countersunk sufficiently deep, one can take them out without difficulty. This is important for cleaning as one need scarcely disturb the birds. The two front panes are separated from each other by a distance of about one-third of an inch, a third pane or firm plate being introduced into corresponding grooves in the centre of the cage which is thus divided in half. The birds fly about in one half, while the cleaning of the other compartment is unhindered. Then the birds are allowed to fly back again and the process is repeated on the remaining half.

Opposite:
Although frightened this tiny Green Thorntail, *Popelairia conversii* (a female weighing 2·2 grams), does not relinquish its perch to the male White-tipped Sicklebill, *Eutoxeres aquila* (enlarged).

Most hummingbirds are 'leaf-bathers'. A refreshing bath on a dewy leaf, what bliss! Land with whirring wings, toboggan down the slope, shake your feathers to make the drops fly and life is good. The Rufous-tailed Hummingbird, *Amazilia tzacatl* (Mexico), likes to cool itself in this way at least once a day.

With a fountain it is even better. First, test the water temperature! Then move right into the middle. (Brown Inca, *Coeligena wilsoni* ♀, Colombia.)

The similarity between the pattern of flower and hummingbird makes an attractive picture (*Lesbia victoriae* ♀ with lady's slipper orchid). Not much larger than a bumble-bee, *Calothorax lucifer* ♀ shows a speed and endurance that baffles description. This tiny creature cost me over two hundred failures before I succeeded in capturing it with my camera.

On both side walls of the showcase there is a small door about nine inches high and five inches broad, covered with wire-netting with a mesh size of one-fifth of an inch. Mosquito netting is not suitable as the cage must be adequately ventilated. The inner side of the walls and the floor are lined with a pale, washable material. Attractively coloured plastic sheets are available. It is not advisable to use a sand-box as for other kinds of birds, or to put any sand on the floor.

In order to see the birds flashing and sparkling in all their beauty, the cages should be lit from the front by tungsten lamps placed high up on either side. These also provide warmth. The showcase is completed by placing a slender branch with not more than one fork in it in each back corner of the cage so that the forks extend towards the front. In a cage thirty inches tall the branches should be set about twenty-two inches above the ground and should be spaced as far as possible from each other. These should be fixed into holes made previously and secured with a thin nail, because they may shrink and fall out when dry. In cages of these dimensions do not use small trees, brushwood or similar impedimenta as they only make cleaning more difficult, and the hummingbirds do not like them. Above all, they like a slender twig out in the open with room in which to fly. One should remember to fix a few hooks for the feeding-bottles (one per bird). Bottles provided with a small tube at the bottom have proved to be reliable. The plastic feeding-bottles with a small red 'shoe' are obtainable in pet shops. (If you cannot find a pet shop that carries them, a national bird organisation such as the National Audubon Society, 1130 Fifth Avenue, New York, NY 10028, can supply them. In Britain they can be obtained from S. H. Travis & Co., 296–300 St John's Street, London, EC1.) They should be washed in hot, not boiling water so that the containers will not warp.

The showcase should stand in a light place, free from draughts and where it is not cold. The best view is obtained by placing it at eye level, roughly where one might put a television set, so that the hummingbirds can provide a colourful display for potential observers. The showcase becomes alive with colour as the small birds fly around, rising and falling in the air or preening and bathing themselves.

Water should be provided for the birds to bathe in. They are attracted to moving water such as a small indoor fountain or a waterfall – of proportionate size – but they also seem to enjoy bathing in a flat saucer containing half an inch of water.

If sufficient space is available, an indoor aviary can be built resembling a kind of winter garden where the birds can fly among tropical plants as though they were in the wild. Many aviculturists dream of keeping their birds in surroundings such as these and an enclosure or greenhouse enables them to realise their dreams. Birds and plants can be kept side by side and a bit of living nature enjoyed in one's own home both winter and summer. Hummingbirds do not possess the tiresome habits of finches, budgerigars and parrots, which regard anything that grows and flowers as desirable food, thus destroying the living plants. Hummingbirds do not nibble or munch.

A layout that will satisfy all that one can wish for requires an alcove or balcony that forms part of a room. Whatever the final layout the showcase should be so designed that it can be kept clean without trouble or waste of time. One should also be able to get into it and move about freely inside. The walls should be painted with a water-resistant, washable paint in a pale warm tone.

Ideally, sheet-zinc should be laid on the floor, with the edges bent upwards two to three inches and hermetically sealed to the wall with plastic resin. After the zinc is treated with dilute acid, it will take lacquer excellently; a floor colour of sandy yellow with brownish mottling looks both natural and unobtrusive. The lacquer gives the floor a smooth surface and a finish that is easy to clean. It is not necessary to spread sand on the floor because the hummingbirds never go down to the ground, and cleaning it with water is hygienic and trouble-free. Although not absolutely essential, it is an advantage to have an outlet drain.

If the winter garden forms part of either a living-room or an office, an ideal way of partitioning it is with a big pane of glass reaching partly or wholly to the ground. Ordinary window-glass is quite adequate. The birds recognise the pane and do not fly into it. A strip of wire-mesh, sufficiently wide to ensure adequate circulation of the air, should be attached to either side of the pane of glass. It is possible to obtain a fine wire-mesh coated with plastic which looks like brass, has an attractive appearance and does not rust. It is a good idea to hang decorative strips of material over the entrance, such as one often sees in Italian cafés, as a safety precaution. These look attractive and even when the door is left open the birds regard them as a barrier.

For dark days or early nights, light can be provided by fluorescent equipment. Lighting of this type is available which uses little current. With one or several ordinary, clear tungsten lamps one can, so to speak, set the hummingbirds alight. Even strong light does not disturb them, nor does it appear to damage their eyes. I have watched them hovering in the air near a small searchlight and virtually flood themselves with light without being blinded. When I found that Herr Reventlow, the late Director of Copenhagen Zoo (a leading expert on hummingbirds), had observed similar behaviour with no ill-effects, I saw no reason to deny my birds the opportunity to play in the light.

Hummingbirds light up only when seen at a certain angle in a certain light. When flying above the observer, they usually appear dark. They are most beautiful when seen at eye level or just below. For this reason I tried at one time to make my aviaries no higher than six feet. Admittedly my visitors and I had the advantage of watching enchanting displays of colour and movement but the birds suffered a corresponding loss in freedom of movement. I finally decided in favour of the birds. It is true that I see them more rarely in their full splendour, but for this very reason the spectacle is even more fascinating, because one sees the full glory of the birds for a fraction of a second and then – before one can really enjoy it – it is suddenly withdrawn. One waits for the next moment and is fortunate if the phenomenon is repeated. So far I have never grown tired of seeing their display of colour and aeronautics.

As one becomes familiar with hummingbirds it is not long before one notices that an individual stands out from the others by its audacious behaviour. It will fly up to you when you arrive with the feeding-bottles, then follow every movement inquisitively and drink from your hand while still flying. This is the individual which should be allowed to fly freely in the house. It does not lose its head and dash at the glass like the others or retire to the seclusion of the curtain for the whole day. It flies round investigating everything in the room even when people are present. It lands without ceremony on the head of the next person. If his hair happens to be unsuitable or too scanty for nest-building it whirs off. It dives under the furniture through a gap only two inches from the floor, swerving up in a clever turn to the typewriter where the red ribbon has to be investigated, and from there flies over to a painting on the wall to examine it closely, preferably a still-life of flowers.

With the help of a feeding-bottle one can entice the humming-bird wherever one wishes, even back into the cage or aviary. It finds a red tube of honey irresistible. The epitome of *la dolce vita* for a hummingbird is a bare branch for take off and landing, and free air space – these are the basic essentials of its existence. Any gnats or fruitflies in the room will be quickly mopped up.

The favourite among my hummingbirds is a Blue-throated Sylph, *Aglaiocercus kingi*, which rules the air space of my study from a small perch that stands in front of me on the desk. A sheet of paper underneath takes care of hygiene. This bird is unaffected by my activities or by my visitors. It even allows itself to be held in the hand. This must be done slowly and gently. For a while it nestles trustingly in the hollow of my hand as though to warm itself. Then it begins to move energetically and buzzes off. A house with flowers and leafy plants makes a very pleasant home for a hum-mingbird. Unless the windows are fitted with wire-mesh they must, of course, remain closed.

A hummingbird that has flown off can be lured back with a feeding-bottle, but this requires a certain amount of luck. One would be much more certain of getting it back if he happened to have an American Indian at hand with a blowpipe, but this is scarcely likely.

Uniform temperature and fresh air

From absolute zero at minus 273 degrees Centigrade to plus twenty million degrees in the centre of the sun there extends a vast range of temperatures inimical to life. The level at which life is capable of existing is indeed alarmingly narrow. The temperature range in which man can survive, even precariously, is scarcely one hundred degrees. The range of temperature at which plant and animal life can thrive in the tropics is even narrower and more critical. The life of hummingbirds hangs by a slender thread.

They cannot tolerate temperatures too high or too low for long. In spite of all their vigour and vitality they must be counted among the most delicate of nature's hothouse creatures. They feel at their best in a steady temperature between twenty and thirty degrees

Centigrade (sixty-eight and eighty-five degrees Fahrenheit). People who are over solicitous and who heat their cages to 'tropical' temperatures of thirty-five degrees, suddenly find their wretched birds sitting on branches longing for cooler conditions. Even in their natural habitat hummingbirds avoid excessive heat. They withdraw into the forest and to streams or remain motionless.

The temperature in the daytime should not be allowed to drop below ten degrees. At night, however, this temperature is sufficient. On one occasion the temperature at which my birds were being kept fell to only five degrees, but they were not harmed.

Since the room temperatures at which humans feel comfortable are approximately right for hummingbirds, much additional heat does not need to be provided. In small cages two ordinary tungsten lamps do good service. In the large indoor aviary I have a 250-watt infrared heater burning during the day. From one corner of the ceiling of the cage it dispenses warmth and red light which makes an attractive effect on the walls and foliage. Perches should be not less than eighteen inches away from such a lamp, plants about double this distance; otherwise they suffer damage.

The birds like to come frequently to the red light. They warm and dry themselves after bathing, fluff themselves, stretch and expose every part of the body, often assuming droll postures in the rays of light. Sometimes they fly up and almost touch the lamps. This really is a most remarkable sight! For several seconds they vibrate and turn like tops in the warmest place. Their plumage stands on end and the hum of their wings is at its highest. They look like little rotating balls. One can sense the ecstasy with which they get warmed through and through. The play lasts three or four seconds, then the bird turns away and seeks a cooler spot. I believe that this type of heating is ideal, for the bird can choose for itself how much and what kind of heat suits it.

Naturally an infrared lamp cannot replace the sun, it only supplies a part of the sun's radiation, namely warmth. Ultraviolet rays are not emitted. Neon tubes produce a small amount of ultraviolet light. To irradiate the birds more strongly one would have to install an ultraviolet lamp. This should be used for only a few minutes a day and even then there is risk of injury to the birds. For this reason I have avoided using an ultraviolet lamp and consequently lost the chance of converting ergosterol to vitamin D, which I now give

113

artificially with the food. If one can site the showcase or aviary in a place which regularly gets the sun so much the better.

Just as draughts can be injurious so too can a stuffy atmosphere deficient in oxygen be unhealthy. Hummingbirds have the highest metabolic rate of all the vertebrates. The oxygen requirement of hummingbirds is exceedingly high because the energy consumption of warm-blooded animals rises in inverse relation to their body weight. In other words the smallest uses relatively the most. Whereas a sleeping man requires 0·2 cubic centimetres of oxygen per hour per gram of body weight, a sleeping hummingbird needs about twenty times as much, namely about four cubic centimetres. When the bird is in flight the consumption of oxygen rises by leaps and bounds. In slow hovering a hummingbird will consume forty-two cubic centimetres per hour for every gram of its body weight. It is estimated that a hummingbird in full action requires up to 165 cubic centimetres of oxygen per gram of body weight every hour. If hummingbirds could speak there is little doubt that when some of them have been dying in captivity their last request would have been for more air.

Home comforts without eucalyptus trees   There are few people who do not wish to have something in their home to reflect the glamour of faraway places, bringing perhaps a suggestion of the warmth and abundance of tropical life to distract them from the bustle of everyday life and the drabness of our civilisation. A small winter garden with a few hummingbirds and luxuriant foliage plants will provide exotic scenery in our homes relieving the grey monotony of reality. The elegant, jewel-like brilliance of the hummingbirds, together with a little of the vegetation which suggests tropical abundance, provides a most attractive picture and if one arranges the birds and plants according to their individual characteristics so that they harmonise, the whole setting will provide endless pleasure to the observer.

It is not possible to reproduce natural conditions completely, and it is therefore better not to adopt a purist attitude about this. For instance, in the wild a single hummingbird will visit one thousand to two thousand flowers a day; it is clearly impossible to grow flowering plants in sufficient numbers to satisfy the food requirements of the hummingbirds. In captivity one could never hope to produce such abundance. It is difficult enough in Europe even to find a eucalyptus tree, let alone bring it to flower.

The important thing is that the bird should feel happy and that maintenance and cleaning should be done with a minimum of effort. Then all will be well.

In my home we use plants with horizontal branches, without too much growth on the underwood and foliage. The hummingbird likes a clear space for take off and landing. It prefers to perch on bare branches at least four inches long of a diameter that is smaller than a pencil. From these it can fly in and out unhindered, and it also has the advantage of being seen better.

An aviary which is too full of plants does not give the bird sufficient room to fly freely and to perform its aerobatics. Space is essential not only for the bird's well-being but it also enables us to enjoy an uninterrupted view of it in flight.

Some species of hummingbird live in tall trees, others keep near to the ground or in a middle stratum. It is therefore necessary to have well grown plants in the aviary with branches almost down to the ground as well as up to the top; each bird can then find the place which suits it best.

The job of cleaning should not take too long. If the plants are sited so that a gangway is left or at least a place that one can stand and turn round in, it should be possible to reach every corner of the aviary without too much effort. It is better to have too few plants than a jungle which in itself becomes a trap for humans.

In my opinion it is not a good idea to make a bed of earth or sand along the bottom and set the plants into it. Mould and decay set in too quickly. To keep such a substrate clean and to renew it regularly would mean endless work. As already mentioned the best floor covering is lacquered zinc plate. It looks nice in a green or yellow, moss or sandy colour and it can be kept clean without difficulty.

The plants are kept in pots. Hanging branches or leaves cover the vessels so that the natural appearance is preserved. The less cluttered the bottom of the aviary, the better.

Plants with woolly, velvety or otherwise rough leaves are not suitable, as particles of dust collect on them and are almost impossible to remove. It is also wise not to have plants with very small leaves as lots of small surfaces take time to clean. Plants with delicate growth that tears or breaks easily should also be avoided. Naturally you will not choose thorny plants for your own comfort. As basic

115

stock one selects plants with large, smooth, leathery or rubbery leaf surfaces.

A plant which is commonly grown as a house-plant and which might have been made for our purpose is *Monstera deliciosa*, a member of the family Araceae. Apart from its lack of flowers this handsome rain-forest plant from Mexico and Guatemala with its plate-size, shiny leaves fulfils all our requirements. Flowering may take place once every ten years. The aerial roots and long leaf stalks of this plant are the traditional perches of the hummingbirds. The decorative leaves can be cleaned easily with a damp sponge. One can turn, bend and tie up these plants as required, according to how they look best. They thrive best in the temperature of a humming-bird aviary. They should be given a good soaking as soon as the pot becomes dry.

Another beautiful and most suitable foliage plant, which may grow to a height of nine feet in a short time, is *Fascedera*, obtainable from nurserymen; it is a treelike ivy species with leathery leaves the size of a man's hand. *Tatra stegma* is another handsome tropical rain-forest plant which is a rank grower: its powerful shoots can grow yards long in a few days, and after only a short time my aviary was festooned with attractive curves and garlands. Its leaves are large and smooth and resemble those of the horse chestnut.

When one has achieved the basic arrangement with three or four tubs of plants, one can perfect the design by leaving appropriate peepholes and spaces. Slender, trailing plants can be grown over the plants of sturdier growth and the danger of fouling is small. The background wall can be decorated with bizarre roots and made attractive with a shelf of pots of flowering plants such as begonia or hibiscus, appropriate to the season. The total impression created will be all the more fabulous if one arranges the finer nuances in the design sparingly and places them at the right distance apart and in relation to the whole set-up. Sometimes a branch of flowering apple is sufficient to create a particularly attractive effect; it also stimulates the interest of the hummingbirds which fly over to inspect it.

It is possible to create a minor work of art in an aviary which will give us a new and deeper understanding of nature. Amongst the coarse and dark rain-forest landscape one can enjoy the contrasting beauty and elegance of the hummingbirds as they dart about against the more sombre background. One can also have the pleasure of seeing them in the gay and more colourful setting of the flower garden where they harmonise with their surroundings. In both settings the hummingbirds will give endless pleasure.

The life of hummingbirds can be described as an extravaganza. These birds differ from others in their methods of feeding, drinking and flying. Their plumage is out of the ordinary and they differ in size and structure, as well as in having different courtship displays and breeding habits.

That they also bathe differently will come as no surprise to anyone who has become accustomed to hearing about their peculiarities. They are very fond of bathing and will do so at every opportunity. It may be that they are aware of their beauty and that an innate vanity makes them take particular care of their plumage, or it may be – as I believe – that instinct drives them to keep their flying equipment meticulously in order, just as careful maintenance is absolutely essential to the efficiency of high performance aircraft. I have the impression, however, that quite apart from its functional aspect, bathing also gives them a great deal of pleasure.

Since they are in their element in the air they do not willingly fly down to the ground to bathe but prefer to do so high up on leaves wet with dew. It does not matter whether the bathtub is formed by a large leaf, lying horizontally or hanging vertically; they turn their breasts towards the leaf surface, shake and flutter their feathers, sometimes almost hovering or lying in the moisture. They press against the leaves and almost rub the water into their plumage with apparent delight; feet, head, wings, tail and even the tongue are dealt with so zealously that one cannot help laughing at them. They slide backwards and forwards on their bellies over the leaves, falling over the edge into the air and righting themselves, only to hurry off to the next switchback where the game begins anew.

To prepare this pleasure for them – and incidentally give oneself a treat – spray the plants with lukewarm water from a sprinkler at least every other day. You will find that the first drops have scarcely collected on the leaves before the birds begin their antics. They are not disturbed if you remain close by.

Apart from this special treat, they should be provided with a shallow dish of water, a large saucer or a plate previously mentioned with about half an inch of water. Some species fly into it; sit down and splash around like sparrows. This is done by *Aglaiocercus kingi*, *Heliodoxa*, *Heliomaster longirostris*, *Lesbia victoriae* and *Colibri coruscans*.

The Sword-billed Hummingbird, *Ensifera ensifera*, in spite of its length, used to prostrate itself in the shallow dish, submerging its bill completely and accomplishing its toilet in this way. Finally it flew over to a ball of wool, which I had suspended as nest material, and wiped its long bill thoroughly, like a knight cleaning his sword after a successful duel. Other hummingbirds, *Amazilia iodura* for instance, make use of a technique peculiar to them. Hovering three feet above the water surface, they suddenly let themselves drop with a splash into the dish, so that they are almost submerged, and then flutter away dripping wet. They repeat this manoeuvre several times in succession.

There are also some species such as *Amazilia tzacatl*, *Chlorostilbon mellisugus*, *Colibri cyanotus*, which dip briefly into the water, and fly in obliquely somewhat in the manner of a swallow. They skim over the water surface like a stone thrown in the game of ducks and drakes.

A brilliant performance of modern bathing technique, half flight, half sailing, was given by *Damophila julie*. While still beating its wings it submerged breast and belly in the water and sailed round in circles like a toy boat or a tiny flying boat. I could never make up my mind whether it was swimming or flying, and even now I am none the wiser.

The most elegant way of taking a bath – patented by hummingbirds – is the 'inverted shower' method. Flying around a small fountain like moths round a lamp, some species hover in the jet of water, allowing themselves to be sprayed from beneath. Now and again they catch individual drops of water in the bill with great skill. To see a crowd of lively hummingbirds dancing above such a fountain is an enchanting sight; the effect is enhanced even more by placing a light in the fountain.

With daily spraying, aided by the fountain and the watering of the plants, I obtained a relative humidity of fifty to fifty-five per cent. These conditions enable the birds and plants to thrive.

Feeding

Nectar or insects? At the height of the season for flowering plants in the natural habitat of hummingbirds, the air hums with the vibrating wings of the birds as they seek nectar. Hundreds of hummingbirds fly into the gardens and orchards, into the tops of wild banana and eucalyptus trees. When the flowering season is over the birds depart and all is quiet again.

From this behaviour it has been assumed that hummingbirds are dependent solely upon nectar in the wild. Based on this assumption, it could be that when the first hummingbirds were kept in captivity people tried feeding them on sugar syrup alone and failed. Fed only on this diet, the birds did not survive more than a few days or at the most a week or two.

People gradually paid more attention to the reports of those observers who recorded that these small birds hunt for insects, diving into swarms of flies like hawks. They also wander about catching flies, small beetles, cicadas, small leaf-bugs and tiny wasps from the leaves. Spiders' webs are sought after and both spiders and their prey, if they are not too large, are released from the webs by the birds.

From these observations it was inferred that the visits to flowers were concerned more with finding the insects which lay hidden in the calyx than with the nectar. This assumption could not be rejected out of hand because, in the fruit blossom most frequently visited by hummingbirds, swarms of flies and small beetles are found but relatively little nectar. The nectar-versus-insect argument grew and biologists, tired of the continual controversy, shot some hummingbirds and examined their stomach contents.

What did they find? Spiders, flies, leaf-bugs, cicadas, little beetles, wasps and ants, but scarcely any nectar!

In 1951 Martin, Zim and Nelson killed more than two hundred hummingbirds and found nothing but insects in their stomachs. But where was the nectar which, without any doubt, the hummingbirds had been drinking, whatever the quantity? It was found that in the first place nectar cannot be proved to be present in the stomach of the bird without special equipment. Secondly, the stomach of a hummingbird has a peculiar shape; the outlet does not lie below as in other birds, but above, directly alongside the entrance to the stomach. The nectar can flow direct to the intestine without passing through the stomach if the stomach is full of insects. So investigation of the stomach contents does not reveal whether birds have taken nectar, and if they have, in what quantity.

The importer of my hummingbirds maintains that eighty per cent of their diet is insects. The results of stomach-content investigations substantiate this opinion. Some of my English friends who keep hummingbirds say that they need masses of insects. But in his book *Hummingbirds*, Mr Greenewalt states that hummingbirds take sugar as their main food.

Having studied these contradictory statements, all that I could be certain of was that hummingbirds require both nectar and insects, but I could not be sure of the quantity or in what proportions they should be given.

A mixed diet but how to do it? The maintenance of hummingbirds in captivity would be no problem if one could offer them nectar-producing flowers and insects in sufficient quantity. The hummingbird would then be in a position to choose a menu according to its taste and in the correct proportions. Unfortunately, neither can be obtained in sufficient quantity. It is therefore necessary to look around for substitutes.

The nectar was the easiest to replace. The birds immediately took a watery solution of honey offered in small coloured drinking phials. The protein part of the diet, the substitute for insects, was much more difficult. Hummingbirds pay no attention to dead food to which other insectivorous birds in captivity become accustomed.

With his ideas on diet, the English aviculturist Alfred Ezra broke fresh ground. He had the idea of mixing proteins, fat, minerals and vitamins with the honey solution in order to replace the deficiency of insects. He used Mellin's Food, a proprietary product which contains several assimilable substances. But this combined food solution had one disadvantage. The bird was forced to consume what it was given, regardless of whether the honey, fat, protein or vitamin had been mixed in undesirable proportions. The bird was therefore not able selectively to follow its own cravings in order to

120

To identify a hummingbird among the 688 subspecies, some of which are very similar, has driven some ornithologists to the brink of despair. This species appears to be an *Amazilia*. Dr Diesselhorst identified it as *Amazilia iodura* (?), but asked me to print the question mark.

Hummingbirds fight strenuously for a perch.
Squawking and buzzing like hornets they
face each other in the air, parrying like
fencers. Their amazing manoeuvres in flight
excel those of any other bird. The
vanquished pitches on to its back, does a roll
and makes off. On the opposite page (much
enlarged), the victor *Damophila julie* ♂, like
a knight in shining armour. Natural size
from head to foot: 1·4 inches, weight
3 grams – but 'every inch a personality'!

Opposite:
It was not easy to achieve this
formal parade of hummingbirds
when they were flying to and fro
and squabbling among themselves.
Nothing disturbed the line-up of
sleeping birds. Above: *Hylocharis
leucotis* ♂, *Acestrura mulsanti* ♀,
Chlorostilbon mellisuga ♂,
Acestrura ♂.

compensate for any particular deficiency.

The food formulae of the following zoos show how many variations of Ezra's basic idea appeared in practice:

Basel Zoo

1000 g water
125 g honey
10 g sugar
45 g condensed milk
3 g meat extract
12 drops vitamins

Berlin Zoo

1000 g water
220 g honey
100 g glucose
12 g milk powder
20 g Nektar–Mil baby food
12 g mealworms
20 g Biosorbin dietetic food
120 g fresh ant pupae
60 g egg yolk (every third day)
12 g Calcipot (calcium preparation)
60 drops vitamins

Cleveland Zoological Park, U.S.A.

1000 g water
60 g honey
10 g condensed milk
5 g carrot
5 g grapes without skins
15 g horse liver
1 g mealworms

Copenhagen Zoo

1000 g water
125 g honey
40 g condensed milk
10 g Mellin's Food
3 g meat extract
5 drops vitamins

Frankfurt Zoo

1000 g water
100 g honey
50 g condensed milk
40 g Alete baby food
12 g germinating wheat
3 g seaweed meal
5 g locusts, mealworms or ant pupae
10 g meat meal
5 g ants' eggs
12 g fresh horse heart or veal
20 g Boviserin (cattle blood serum)
$\frac{1}{2}$ raw egg
$\frac{1}{4}$ apple
$\frac{1}{4}$ banana
$\frac{1}{4}$ orange
$\frac{1}{4}$ raw carrot
2 lettuce leaves
250 mg canthaxanthin–Rovimix mixture
20 drops Polyvital
0·25 g edible calcium

125

Krefeld Zoo

1000 g water
125 g honey
10 g sugar
45 g condensed milk
3 g meat extract
12 drops vitamins

London Zoo

1000 g water
130 g honey
2 g Hepovite (liver extract)
40 g Complan (proprietary food)
2 drops vitamins

Stuttgart Zoo

1000 g water
140 g honey
20 g condensed milk
2 g meat extract
16 drops vitamins

Wuppertal Zoo

1000 g water
70 g honey
20 g raw cane sugar
10 g rusk meal
15 g Nestlé's milk
2 g meat extract

Although no quantities are given, the following concoction prepared by Professor König of the Wilhelminenburg Biological Station, Vienna (*Gefiederte Welt* for September 1959), is of interest: water in a 1 : 1 ratio to the other substances, honey in the same volume as the following ingredients:

dried shrimps
silkworm pupae
Daphnia
blood-, fish- and bone-meal
wheat seedlings
dried liver

mealworms
fresh ant pupae
eggs with shells
sometimes horse heart,
banana, apple, carrot, lettuce
vitamins

At first sight these ten recipes are a veritable hotchpotch. For better or for worse, the bird must accept one or another of these diets; they are prepared in a mixer and dispensed as a somewhat sweet-tasting liquid of fairly low viscosity. My compliments to these little birds which have to swallow it all.

There are considerable differences in detail between the formulae: in 1000 g water, carbohydrates (honey and other forms of sugar) may be either 60 g or 350 g protein either 3 or 30 g combined vitamins either 2 or 50 drops. These differences may have considerable effect on the health and well-being of the birds. There is

126

general agreement on only one point, namely, that the substitute for nectar forms the main constituent. Since the honey, that is, the invert sugar, is predominant in every recipe it suggests that the experience of the zoological gardens supports the view of those biologists who maintained that hummingbirds live mainly on flower nectar. There is considerable lack of clarity as regards the relative amounts of water, honey, protein, fat and vitamins.

Long-term observations on record-breakers

I decided to let my hummingbirds supply the answers to what they wanted to eat and how much. Above all, it was important for me to find out the highest amount of fat and protein that would be beneficial to them and the approximate amounts of sugar and water which a hummingbird needs every day relative to its body weight.

I conducted a series of experiments for a period of three years, in which thirty different species of hummingbird were involved in providing the answers.

To begin with, I had to find out which bird was the most zealous insect eater, and then the quantity of insects it actually consumed per day. In other words, having discovered the bird with the largest appetite for insects, I wanted to ascertain its maximum demand for protein and fat when feeding under conditions which enabled it to choose between honey and insects.

At the beginning of the experiment I fed the birds for several days on one of the mixtures recommended by the zoos but gave them only a small amount of protein and fat in order to make them avid for insects. When I subsequently released fruitflies (*Drosophila*) in large swarms into the aviary, the birds eagerly began to hunt them. For three days I made observations on each species and I found that the particularly active hunters were the species of *Amazilia*, *Aglaiocercus*, *Boissonneaua*, *Coeligena* and also *Lesbia victoriae*. However these were all surpassed in zeal, skill and success by a male *Hylocharis leucotis*.

I caught this bird and isolated it. This also involved isolating myself because I did not want to take my eyes off it for a period of ten days. I absented myself from my job, took leave of my family and sat down in front of a special glass cage where I could watch what happened. My son undertook to supply both the hummingbird and myself with anything else that was needed.

The bird, a male *Hylocharis leucotis*, weighed three grams; it was

127

in superb condition and had been in my possession for six months. It had undergone one moult and was an excellent flier and active singer.

The observation cage was a glass box twice the size of a television set, with a front panel of glass and the rear and side walls were covered with a pale glossy material. White paper was laid along the bottom and repeatedly replaced with fresh sheets. An upright twig provided the sole perching place for the bird. The feeding-bottle was a small commercial type plastic tube with a red base.

At last everything was ready and on the evening of 24 December 1964 I put the bird into the observation cage.

26 DECEMBER

1130 hrs Removal of all food.

1330 hrs Start of continuous observations, sitting with my nose glued to the glass, writing materials on a table in front of me. The bird which has now fasted for two hours remains quiet. It watches me.

1335 hrs Control paper underneath the bird removed. Fresh white paper laid out.

1355 hrs The paper is still clean. No more droppings.

1400 hrs Feeding bottle offered, containing the following:

1. The 'honey only' experiment

In 30 cc of lukewarm (previously boiled) water:
    3 g honey
    1 drop Multibionta (a vitamin preparation)

Time	Period of drinking in seconds	Droppings O = clear Y = yellowish	Remarks
1400	11	O	Drinks greedily without stopping
1405		O	
1410	4		
1413		Y	
1414	9		Stretches before each take-off
1418		Y	

128

The above details represent the first notes which I made. The observations, however, were continued in the same manner up to 2300 hours.

2300 hrs Lights put out until the next morning at 0700 hrs when they were switched on again. Continuous observation and recording were then resumed until 1400 hrs. Thus ended the first 16-hour day of the bird. (This was the period of time used in all my experiments.)

Results of the 'honey only' experiment

An astonishing performance for so little sustenance!

In 16 hours the bird drank 172 times
On average it drank every 5·4 minutes
Average duration of each drink, 5 seconds
Longest duration of a drink, 11 seconds
Shortest duration of a drink, 1 second
Longest period of rest, 12 minutes
Shortest period of rest, less than 1 minute
First liquid droppings after the first drink, after 5 minutes
First firm dropping, after 13 minutes

Of the sixteen hours the bird spent fifteen on the wing. The remainder of the food solution still contained 0·5 g honey.

Honey consumption: 2·5 g = 80% of its body weight
Water consumption: 25 g = 830% of its body weight

The control, showing how much water would evaporate from the feeding-bottle in the same period, showed practically nil. The evaporating surface is minute and the bottle is closed at the top.

I repeated the same experiment a few months later on two different days with the same bird. On one of these days it took 66 per cent of its body weight as honey and 73 per cent on the other.

Behaviour of the bird

The flight to the feeding-bottle occurred with great regularity and took up almost all the bird's time. In the first half of the sixteen hours the bird searched the cage repeatedly for other feeding places. It also flew to the corners of the cage and by threat manoeuvres apparently tried to rouse insects which were not there.

At first it sang now and again. In power and duration, however, this song could not compare with what the bird had previously produced the whole day long without any effort. The bird yawned very frequently – more than fifty times. I was particularly struck by this, as previously I had rarely observed yawning to take place. It also stretched itself before each take-off. In the second half of the sixteen-hour period the bird no longer hunted for food and no longer sang. Towards the end of the feeding period, it looked unwell, its eyes were no longer bright, its plumage was somewhat ruffled and, apart from flights to the food, it was very quiet. This occurred in the morning, a time when the bird would normally have been particularly active.

In summing up the results, it must be pointed out that the bird lost its vitality astonishingly fast when fed only on honey. Over a period of time it would eventually have become sick and died.

2. The 'honey and insect' experiment

It was with considerably more pleasure that I was able to start the bird on the second experiment. A born flycatcher, it would now have the opportunity to catch flies to its heart's content. It would also get honey which it doubtless also enjoyed, but the choice would be left to the bird itself.

In 30 cc water
  3 g honey   }   as previously
  1 drop Multibionta
In addition, fruitflies (*Drosophila*) in large swarms

The observations on this experiment extended over six days, of sixteen hours each, until I ran out of flies.

27 DECEMBER 1964

1405 hrs Fresh feeding-bottle with honey placed in position. The first jars of fly culture, prepared earlier, are brought up from our heated cellar by my son. (Hundreds of flies had already found their way into the kitchen to the delight(!) of my wife.) The first jar was soon opened and as the huge cloud of flies flew into the cage, my son hopped from one leg to the other in excitement. The giant swarm hums in the cage. Each individual fly can be seen clearly against the brightly illuminated white floor and pale background. Each time a fly is definitely caught a tick is made in my notes.

Up to the final day of the experiment there was so much living food available all the time that the bird was continuously surrounded by a small swarm. In order to arrive at a maximum catch I had fastened a piece of banana under the twig which served as a perch. In this way the flies were enticed into the immediate vicinity of the bird.

130

Time	Period of drinking in seconds	Flies definitely caught and swallowed	Droppings O = clear Y = yellowish X = black, firm	Remarks
1405	5			Bottle hung up
1409			O	
1410		21		Flies released
1412	3			Dives into swarm like a hawk
1413		11		
1414	4			
1418		2		
1419	5	2	X	First dropping with chitinous remains
1423	7	6	Y	

During my occasional unavoidable absences of a minute or so at a time, my son continued to keep the record. Although he has a lively mind his school results can be described as only moderate for a senior pupil. As I had little fault to find with his counting of the flies, I took this to be a sign that he must find other things of more interest than school lessons.

Result of the 'honey and insect' experiment

The average of the six days gave the following results for a sixteen-hour day:

In 16 hours the bird drank 267 times

It drank on average every 3·6 minutes

Average period of drinking per meal, 3·5 seconds

Longest 9 seconds

Shortest about 1 second

Longest period of rest, 10 minutes

Shortest period of rest, less than 1 minute

First liquid excretion, after 4 minutes

First droppings with chitin, after 14 minutes.

Honey consumption: 2·2 g = 73% of its body weight.

In spite of the flies caught as additional food the consumption of sugar remained almost unaltered at an astonishingly high level.

131

Consumption of flies: an average of 677 per day.

This is an impressive total, if one balances it against the expenditure of energy and the aeronautic skill involved in making every individual catch. A swarm of six hundred and seventy-seven fruitflies is gigantic. Thus it is readily understandable that when attempting to estimate such a consumption of insects, observers can make errors. As the bird took an average of forty-two flies every hour, its small stomach was naturally always full, while the honey immediately flowed over into the intestine. My wife's reaction to this, however, was that the many flies must surely be heavier than the small amount of honey consumed by the bird.

One should not rely only on a visual impression and, if I may venture an opinion on such a touchy subject, one should never rely on woman's intuition. To the housewife a hundred fruitflies in the kitchen are like a plague of locusts and they represent a major catastrophe, whereas a drop containing two grams of honey is scarcely noticed. A woman is naturally biased on this subject and prejudice dies hard. In order to settle the argument with my wife, I had to defer the problem of whether fruitflies or honey represent more to the hummingbird to no less an authority than the Munich College of Technology. But before giving their results, a few comments on the behaviour of the bird during the 'honey and insect' experiment are relevant.

Behaviour of the bird

During this second experiment, the bird was transformed from a sickly, silent individual into one that sparkled with life, performing masterly aerobatics and singing with a zest that was a delight to hear. The bird could not have been more full of life. When it chased a fly energetically, it caught it. It followed every twist and turn that the insect made. It is true that sometimes the bird had to make three or four thrusts with gaping bill before it caught its prey, but it did not give up until it had succeeded.

It was only when the edge of its appetite was appeased that it became more selective. It would come up behind an insect and look at it before snapping it up. If the fly was too large it did not take it. My wife's interpretation of this was that the bird was sparing the females. I saw no reason to disenchant her. The bird showed a preference for catching the insects in flight. Although it took them off the walls and the glass, using the tip of the bill like a pair of

132

foreceps, it did so only after trying unsuccessfully to chase them out by vibrating its wings. The behaviour of the flies was also worthy of note. When the bird was in the air, they hurried to get to the wall where they remained quietly. They did not swarm again until after the bird perched.

During the first experiment the bird had yawned frequently. This it no longer did and it also stretched itself less frequently; its eyes were bright and its plumage glossy. It sang and hunted almost without interruption. Its meals always followed its own bill of fare: after it had caught one or several flies in sudden sorties, it would always take a sip from the feeding-bottle.

One interesting observation deserves to be mentioned. There were usually a few fruitflies crawling about on and in the red base of the feeding-bottle. Sometimes one even fell into the liquid. But the hummingbird never touched one of these 'adjacent' flies. In visiting the feeding-bottle it was interested only in the honey solution.

One is forced to the conclusion that hummingbirds visit flowers only on account of the nectar, and not, as has often been thought, because of the insects living within them.

Scientists can determine the amount of flesh in a fruitfly very simply: they kill the flies with ether, count out one hundred and fifty clean specimens and weigh them on an analytical balance.

Weight of 150 flies: 180 mg

Result: 1·2 mg per fly

The weight of the 677 flies eaten on one day by my *Hylocharis leucotis* is therefore: 0·8 g = 27% of the bird's weight.

I reared another large batch of these flies for scientific analysis. The flies were first dried for one and a half hours at more than 130 degrees Centigrade. The following results were sent to me.

The flies consisted of:

60% water	6·5% fat
22% chitin	0·5% undetermined carbohydrates, min-
11% protein	erals and trace elements

Thus a fruitfly weighing 1·2 milligrams gives only one to two ten-thousandths of a gram of flesh. This seems a remarkably small amount, but evidently my *Hylocharis* thought them worth the trouble, for it caught 677 in a single day. All in all – taking into account water, honey and insects – our experimental guinea pig *Hylocharis* took on the average the following substances per day:

| 22·0 g water from the honey solution | |
| 0·5 g water from the flies | |

22·5	g water	= 750%	of its body weight
2·2	g honey	= 73%	of its body weight
0·09	g protein	= 3%	of its body weight
0·052	g fat	= 2%	of its body weight
0·176	g chitin	= 6%	of its body weight
25·018	g total taken in	= 834%	of its body weight

As I discovered later with the help of a further series of experiments, the amount of water offered, which appeared to me to be relatively too high, could be reduced to about half.

To this day my wife mistrusts the results of the analysis because she was so impressed by the vast quantities of flies. Nevertheless experiment showed clearly that, even taking into account the gigantic number of insects available and consumed, a hummingbird lives mainly on invert sugar.

Since the bird was free to choose what it ate, one can say, by and large, that the relative amounts of these foodstuffs represent the combination required by a hummingbird. The bird was in fine condition. There are certainly some hummingbirds which hunt fewer insects, and others which catch more spiders than flies, and therefore attain a somewhat higher consumption without additional effort. However, these differences are not so great that they make any significant difference in the basic ratio of invert sugar (nectar or honey) to fat and protein.

3. The 'excessive fat and protein' experiment

I wanted to test the reactions of my *Hylocharis leucotis* on one further aspect of diet before bringing my other hummingbirds into the picture. In the first experiment, it had shown me how it reacted to a diet of honey only, namely, by being miserable after an initial enthusiasm and a big feast on nectar. In the second experiment, it had shown the effect of enjoying a mixed diet in natural proportions by regaining its vigour and exhibiting brilliant form. Now it was to be subjected to a mixture which, relative to the honey, contained twice the amount of the other substances, that is, fat, protein, higher carbohydrates and roughage.

30 g water	
3 g honey	as in experiments 1 and 2
1 drop Multibionta	

2 g egg yolk
1 g mealworms
1 g bovine blood serum
1 g powdered milk
1 g banana
plus living fruitflies

These ingredients were blended in a mixer and yielded a liquid of low viscosity, a yellowish juice with a pleasant, slightly sickly smell.

Time	Drinking period in seconds	Flies caught and swallowed	Excretion	Remarks
1410				Food offered. Only short sips. Repeated attempts, head shaking, gives up.
1415				Fresh attempt to drink, stops immediately.
1416				Searches around the bottle.
1417				Another attempt.
1421				More sips, without proper drinking.
1422	3			Drinks.

Result of the 'excessive fat and protein' experiment

In 16 hours the bird drank about 182 times
It drank every 5 minutes
Average duration of each drink, 4 seconds
Longest duration of a drink, 12 seconds
Shortest, less than 1 second
Longest period of rest, 13 minutes
Shortest, less than 1 minute
First excretion of firm droppings, after 20 minutes

In 16 hours about 25·6 grams of the available 39 grams were drunk and 81 flies were caught.
Analysis of the 25·6 g:

19·6 g water	=	653% of the body weight
2·0 g honey	=	67% of the body weight
4·0 g other substances (fat, protein, carbohydrate etc)	=	103% of the body weight
0·1 g flies	=	3% of the body weight

135

In a single day the little bird had taken a total of 856% of its body weight in water and food. I would not have believed such a prodigious amount possible unless I had witnessed it myself, worked out all my records and double-checked everything.

Behaviour of the bird after the 'excessive fat and protein' experiment

Although it only drank this food mixture unwillingly, the regularity and duration of the bird's flights for food were unaltered. In the intervals, however, it presented a sorry sight. Mostly it squatted motionless, crouching on its perch; it no longer sang and rarely preened itself and there was no sign of its previous effervescent vitality. Even the flies, which had previously aroused enthusiasm for a whole week, never caused any excitement. It merely snapped up what could be reached without effort.

The bird looked tired and sick. It appeared troubled by the enormous task of digesting the food and was incapable of making an effort to do anything else. It was like a man who has celebrated too well and who wants only to rest, sleep and digest his heavy meal. As it was obvious that prolonging the indigestible food would have harmed the bird if continued over a period, I broke off the experiment prematurely.

But why then, one may ask, did the bird drink so much? It would seem that it would have taken considerably less if the food was so rich and difficult to digest. But no! It drinks itself almost to death. Why?

The appetite of the bird appears in the first place to be centred on sugar. It tries – come what may – to attain an intake of at least 60 to 70 per cent of its body weight per day. If other substances are mixed with the honey, the bird is forced to accept these until it has taken in its quota of sugar.

Brown Inca as taster

Opposite: *Heliodoxa rubinoides* (Colombia), a handsome hummingbird which flies very fast. Here I have deliberately renounced the chance of photographing the ruby-red patch on the throat in order to show for once the elegant profile of this beautiful bird.

After my experiments with insects had provided me with an approximate scale for mixing the honey, protein and fat, according to the natural requirements shown in the experiments, I still lacked more precise data on the water component. An excess could lead to trouble over a period of time. On this point the figures given by different zoos are widely divergent as shown by the extremes which I have extracted.

Berlin Zoo: 565 g food in 1000 g water = ca. 5 : 10
Cleveland Zoo: 96 g food in 1000 g water = ca. 1 : 10

This Blue-throated Sylph flies to my daughter's mouth, showing no fear of such a large creature and presumably taking the redness of her lips to be a nectar-dispensing flower.

When I provokingly placed a stuffed Long-eared Owl in the vicinity of an incubating Brown Inca, the hummingbird immediately attacked it. The anger of the tiny creature is quite apparent: the bill presented like a foil, the plumage fluffed out and the tail feathers spread in agitation. The hummingbird shot at the owl like an arrow from the bow.

A male Velvet-purple Coronet, *Boissonneaua jardini* (Colombia) on a flower of *Heliconia jacquinii*, a relative of the bananas from northern South America. This favourite flower of hummingbirds yields abundant nectar which is greedily sipped by the birds.

One zoo works with ten times as much water as the rest of the components, the other with only two times as much water. Which is correct?

Once again I decided to let my hummingbirds supply the answer, this time using all the birds in my possession. (The sterling *Hylocharis* had in the meantime been returned to the freedom of the big communal aviary.) I first fed them all with a much-diluted solution. On the following days I systematically reduced the amount of water at the rate of 100 cubic centimetres per day. I then waited until the birds became so thirsty that they were forced to slake their thirst by drinking pure water at the fountain.

Day	Food in grams	Water in grams	
1	100	1000	None drank extra water
2	100	900	None drank extra water
3	100	800	None drank extra water
4	100	700	None drank extra water
5	100	600	None drank extra water
6	100	500	None drank extra water
7	100	400	A few drank extra water
8	100	300	More drank extra water
9	100	200	Busy traffic at the water fountain
10	100	100	All the birds drank extra water

From this behaviour I believe I can conclude that their requirements are met by a mixture with a ratio of food to water of 1 : 4 or 1 : 5, and that more water is excessive.

To summarise the position, the results so far gave the following basic rules for an artifical food mixture in relation to the body weight of the bird.
  (a) 400% water
  (b) 70% honey
  (c)   3% protein
       2% fat
       6% trace elements, minerals, vitamins, roughage

(a) *The water*   The water should be poured into the mixture when lukewarm, not hot.

141

(b) *The honey*   In the wild hummingbirds collect flower nectar, not honey. What is the difference?

The only significant difference is the higher water content of the nectar, which bees reduce to twenty per cent in changing it to honey. In addition, they break up the cane sugar contained in some nectars, by means of the enzymes in their saliva, into simpler molecules.

Apart from the pollen, which occurs in traces, honey is even more easily digested than nectar. Ten grams of honey contain a few milligrams of pollen which is rich in vitamins and nutriment. It is doubtful whether hummingbirds can utilise this substance, because the pollen grains are surrounded by a covering which is resistant to the digestive juices. Honey is equal in value to the nectar and is one of the best foods that nature offers. As one of the best energy providers it is quickly and completely absorbed. Certain constituents of honey also serve in protecting against disease vectors, others in various growth processes in the body. So as daily sustenance nothing better could be offered to the hummingbirds. Honey is a valuable mixture in itself and if sugar or industrial glucose is used it would only be diluting the value of the honey. In the wild hummingbirds do not always visit the same flowers so the types of honey should be varied.

(c) *Protein, fat and other substances*   The following investigations, extending over a period of three years, were intended to show which substances were suitable as a replacement for the insects which are usually in short supply, and whether the basic formula would achieve success with a large number of hummingbird species over a period of time.

As a substitute for insects, it was once recommended that I put a whole sparrow or a mouse, complete with skin, through a mixer and add the resultant pulp to the hummingbirds' food. However, I regard this as being just as barbaric as putting an elephant through a mixer, then pouring the result into bottles for babies, because babies need proteins and other substances as well as carbohydrates.

The basic principle of offering as many different nutrients as possible is doubtless correct. But I consider it to be quite impossible for the digestive organs of a hummingbird, which in the wild deal only with insects of the most delicate structure, to be capable of digesting such coarse structures as horn and bone. Thus, I even

142

consider that whole hens' eggs with the shells are unsuitable.

Nutrients which fulfilled the following requirements had to be found and tested:

1. They should contain animal and plant protein from as many different sources as possible, as well as fats, small amounts of higher carbohydrates (such as occur in the stomach contents of insects), trace elements, minerals, vitamins and some roughage, which is also important in digestion.
2. They should be soluble in water or at least form a colloidal suspension, that is, remain floating in the liquid in finely divided form, so that, sip by sip, the bird obtains a standard, homogeneous mixture.
3. They should taste good to the bird.
4. They should be easily digestible and cause neither constipation nor diarrhoea, nor other disturbances of the digestive tract.
5. The birds should feel well and develop properly.

I found a wealth of potential substances in the feeding instructions of the various zoos. I must confess that I have not tasted the food mixtures myself, although there have been heroes among research workers and aviculturists who have not shrunk from their duty when put to the test.

The role of taster was taken over by a Brown Inca, *Coeligena wilsoni*. When the feeding-bottles were taken into the aviary and placed on a row of small sticks, this bird flew over and took a sip from each one of them to see what kind of a cocktail they contained. In most other birds the sense of taste is not particularly well developed, but a hummingbird reacts immediately to the slightest change in the taste of its usual sugary liquid.

If the first bottle tasted good, the hummingbird remained at it. On the other hand, if it tasted slightly less sweet than usual, it tried its luck at another bottle and, on finding nothing better there, it accepted what was offered and took it contentedly. If the food tasted sour, it drew back and shook itself. After several attempts of this nature, hunger forced it to drink. If, however, the taste was too unpleasant, the bird shot off after the first sip and flew to its perch, ruffled its feathers and would have nothing further to do with the feeding-bottle. When this happened I had to begin all over again with a new mixture.

143

The Brown Inca tasted the following foods with its delicate tongue
before it allowed its companions to get at the food:

1. mealworms
2. white of egg
3. egg yolk
4. meat extract
5. liver extract
6. blood serum
7. powdered milk
8. and 9. combined feeding compounds
10. ready-made baby food

I tested all these foods one by one. I mixed them with a
honey-and-water solution and gave them to the birds to drink for
ten consecutive days. There was, therefore, always a ten-day run
and I was delighted when all the birds reached the end of it in good
condition.

In order to avoid too violent an alteration to diet, I changed the
food gradually between experiments. Reckoning the quantity was
simple. Based on the previous analyses, an adequate amount of the
mixture was given – containing 400 per cent water, sixty per cent
honey, three per cent protein and two per cent fat – in proportion
to the weight of the bird's body.

The volume of the prepared mixture was measured and the
constituents noted. The birds had a sixteen-hour drinking day at the
end of which the unconsumed portion was measured. As evapor-
ation was effectively nil, the difference gave the actual amount
consumed.

The majority of these ingredients, however, brought no satisfactory result. When mixed only with the honey solution, they
either affected the taste so strongly that the birds refused to take it or
the mixture was not homogeneous. For instance, with mealworms,
egg yolk or liver extract, individual particles of each component
floated to the surface of the liquid or sank to the bottom. Thus the
birds received too much or too little of certain substances, and were
overfed or remained hungry. Other substances, for example
powdered milk, caused digestive troubles. The faeces were hard and
bulky and the birds suffered from constipation.

The commercial dried milk products proved relatively good; they contained carefully balanced amounts of essential, easily digested nutrients and remained homogeneous in the mixture. From these the best result was obtained with a ready-mixed baby food, Nektar-Mil II, mixed with the honey solution.

In view of this I will give only the details of the last experiment and will not describe the earlier experiments, which were concerned with investigating other substances.

Ready-mixed baby food

Nektar-Mil II

Manufacturer: Milupa-Pauly GmbH, Friedrichsdorf Ts, West Germany

Description: a very fine yellowish powder with a pleasant smell of honey

Electron microscope examination revealed that the starch component from whole wheat is broken up by dextrinisation and divided into very small, easily digested particles. Protein is available from the milk and also from plant albuminoid.

Composition:
- 49% invert sugar (mainly honey and lactose)
- 16% protein
- 15·5% fat
- 12% higher carbohydrates
- 7·5% minerals, trace elements and vitamins from the milk, honey and whole wheat

The nutrients honey and Nektar-Mil, together with water, were mixed in a proportion which corresponded closely with the basic principle derived from the 'honey-plus-insect experiment' (400% water, 70% honey, 3% protein, etc., in relation to the body weight of the bird). Sometimes twice the amount of probable consumption was offered. Twenty-two hummingbirds, consisting of fourteen different species ranging from the smallest to the largest, with a total body weight of 101·5 grams, were concerned in this experiment:

Amount of food offered daily:

In 800 g water:

   121 g honey

    38 g Nektar-Mil containing:

       18·5 g invert sugar

        6·0 g protein

```
      5·9 g fat
      4·6 g higher carbohydrate
      2·9 g minerals trace elements, vitamins
      ─────
      37·9 g
```

Average daily use per 16-hour day:

		Percentage of body weight
492 g water		485
74 g honey	⎫	84
11·4 g invert sugar	⎬	
3·7 g protein		3·6
3·6 g fat		3·5
2·8 g higher carbohydrate		2·7
1·8 g minerals, etc.		1·7

The consumption was about twenty per cent higher than in the case of the *Hylocharis leucotis* which was previously kept on its own. Evidently competition for food and the consequent increased activity caused a higher consumption.

Solubility: this mixture remained homogeneous. There was no separation of particles to the surface or to the bottom.

Taste: good. The birds took well to the mixture from the beginning.

Digestion: perfectly satisfactory. Faeces yellowish, pastelike.

Behaviour of the birds: the birds were lively and active, without being too aggressive. They were in particularly fine condition towards the end of this last ten-day run.

Result: this mixture appeared to meet the stated requirements best. It also kept better than the others and did not become sour overnight.

Summary: the birds had certainly shown that they would take the most varied additives to the honey solution, but that with an overdose of fat, protein and roughage they reacted with signs of lassitude and sickness and lost weight.

Although Complan also appeared to me to be suitable, I decided at the end of the ten-day tests to carry on with a long series of experiments with Nektar-Mil. It seemed to me that in Nektar-Mil the content of invert sugar and the whole wheat – which is of special value physiologically and easily digestible since it is broken down – were significantly more advantageous than the raw sugar component in Complan. With the Nektar-Mil mixture I had found a basic food, a daily sustenance for my hummingbirds.

I now stuck to this basic recipe for some months, viz.,

800 g water   121 g honey   38 g Nektar-Mil II

I added varying small amounts of other substances to the food each day, with the sole objective of varying the taste and rounding off the mixture. Thus, I reduced the Nektar-Mil component by about five to eight grams, and as an alternative I gave the corresponding amounts of meat extract, Complan, protein, Biosorbin, Boviserin, live insects and so on. Sometimes I also gave some banana, lettuce, peach or grapes and, occasionally, pear and apple.

With these variants, I scarcely altered the total proportions of nutrient as already laid down. The essential amino acids were never given in overdose because I did not want to create an imbalance. Also, I only used vitamin additives extremely sparingly. I thought that I ought to restrict myself to small quantities because the honey itself, the Nektar-Mil and the other substances are rich in vitamins.

I gave ten drops of Multibionta (manufactured by E. Merck, Darmstadt, West Germany) in 800 grams of water daily and during the moult ten drops of T-Vitazell (E. Tosse & Co., Hamburg-Wandsbek, West Germany).

Some zoological gardens give their hummingbirds only honey and water in the evening, in order to avoid the spoiling of food overnight. With Nektar-Mil this restriction is not necessary. There is a big advantage, in my opinion, in letting the birds have uninterrupted access to a standard nutritious food mixture. They are particularly active in the evenings as well as in the mornings; in the wild they hunt for insects in the evening and it is therefore at this time of day that their need for food is particularly great.

The daily ration of food was prepared in the mixer in the morning, two-thirds of it being poured into the feeding-bottles and given to the birds, while the last third was preserved in the refrigerator until late afternoon; after removing the remains of the daytime ration and cleaning the bottles, the remainder was then given to them for supper and breakfast.

I followed this method of feeding for a period of two years, and I could not have wished for better results. I was not able to specify which food components the birds effectively absorbed or to what extent they were able to break down the larger molecules of protein into amino acids or whether their enzymes had been able to split up the higher carbohydrates. Nevertheless, I could at least say that – with very few exceptions – the hummingbirds were alive and had remained healthy. They not only survived but regularly renewed their plumage. Some species, for example my two male *Aglaiocercus kingi*, were even more resplendent after the moult than before. During the breeding season all the males made display flights, quite apart from whether a female of the same species was present or not. The singers among them twittered away throughout the year. Five species (*Coeligena wilsoni, Damophila julie, Chrysolampis mosquitus, Aglaiocercus kingi* and *Amazilia tzacatl*) built nests in the communal aviary; two of them (*Coeligena* and *Damophila*) laid four eggs each in one year, which they incubated for the full period.

From these results I came to the conclusion that the kind of artificial food mixture which I provided, and the relative proportions of its constituents, approximated to the natural diet of hummingbirds in the wild.

Behaviour

Knight without fear and blemish

One might assume that tiny creatures which are adorned like flowers and jewels, that feed placidly and appear delicate and gentle in all their movements, would also be peaceable by nature; one would expect them to be submissive in their demeanour and to willingly give way to strangers. This, however, would be a mistake for there is nothing placatory about a hummingbird. I have known birds such as budgerigars, exotic finches, starlings, thrushes, sunbirds, tanagers, quails and pheasants, which I have kept in captivity, but none of these equalled the indefatigable courage and robust toughness of the hummingbird. Even the ordinary sparrow, the so-called guttersnipe of the bird world, cannot compare with the hummingbird.

They defend furiously anything that belongs to them and attack what does not belong to them with equal determination. They use up more energy than any other bird, their metabolism is the highest and their hunger is the greatest. When they find a tree, a bush or a flowering shrub in the wild – or a bottle of their honey in captivity, which to them is the equivalent of food for the gods – they claim it for their own. Every other hummingbird, even if double its size, is usually subjected to a sudden and furious attack. Like a pistol-shot the 'owner' rushes at its opponent. It aims directly at the body of its adversary and dashes at full speed towards it. This attack takes place at such lightning speed that however hard I looked I could never be sure of exactly what happened at the moment of impact.

It seems certain, however, that the attacker seldom uses its long pointed bill, which it carries in front like a lance, as a weapon. This instrument is not adapted for this kind of operation, it is too sensitive and the danger is too great that the attacker might itself sustain an injury. The attack on the other hummingbird is carried out with the claws. Whether the victim is struck or not, the latter does not think of quitting the field of action. It responds with a rapid display, readies itself for aerial combat, and strikes back. The antagonists make an enchanting picture, two diminutive and sparkling knights with foils at the ready, facing each other in the air. They thrust and retreat, fighting with all the tricks and feints of fencing whether in the rule book or not. One can observe them trying to get at each other with their sharp pointed claws. If they make contact, they sometimes tumble to the ground locked together and fight on like street urchins. Sometimes they lie still for a moment on the ground, as though stunned, but they do not release their grip on each other. Fearing for their safety, I often used to rush over to separate them. But as I came closer, they would fly up and continue to fight in the air without paying any attention to me.

While building its nest, my Brown Inca (*Coeligena wilsoni*) spent half its time driving off other birds. In its attacking flight, I observed a peculiarity which I have not seen in any of the other birds. As it reached its opponent in a furious onslaught, I could hear a distinct clap, sounding like someone clapping his hands. The bird was travelling so fast that one could not see what made the sound. At first I thought that the bird produced this loud noise with its crop, which was much distended when attacking. It is, however, more likely that it claps its wings together and thus gives its adversary a symbolic box on the ear. It is still astonishing that it can produce such a sharp sound with a relatively small wing surface. They fight doggedly, delivering and also receiving angry blows. There are some more peaceable species than *Coeligena wilsoni* but when attacked even these become vigorous and aggressive for as long as the attack lasts.

There is only one thing which can sap their energy and weaken their desire to fight: this is when they are kept from their feeding place too often and for too long. For this reason care must always be taken to see that each bird has its own bottle at which it can drink undisturbed. If you watch where a particular bird usually goes when it is pursued, you will see that this is where it is left in peace; this is the place in which to hang up its bottle, preferably in such a position that it can drink while perching. A hovering hummingbird usually is attacked but rarely one that is perching quietly by a bottle.

They not only attack members of their own group fearlessly, but they will sometimes attack birds of prey, humans, cats or anything that invades an area in which they are interested. Hummingbirds have even been observed to fly very close to falcons, repeatedly making bold flight manoeuvres near them and forcing these fast and agile predators to turn aside.

I once let a cat into the aviary to put the hummingbirds to a test. The drama which followed had to be seen to be believed. After a few pitiable attempts to catch them, the poor animal did not know into which corner to slink!

There are also several reports of humans being so closely mobbed by angry hummingbirds that they could feel the currents of air produced by the wings. Hummingbirds rely on their superior powers of flight in everything they do, like impudent street urchins who trust to their nimble legs to make good their escape.

Not sociable, but needing company The behaviour of hummingbirds in captivity is something of a contradiction: they behave like tough soldiers of fortune, seeking neither affection nor tenderness. It is no use expecting them to show any friendliness towards other individuals or to give any sign of seeking warmth in others. There is no billing and cooing such as we have come to expect from other caged birds, like budgerigars and exotic finches. Each one keeps strictly to itself. Any approach from another individual is regarded as an intrusion on its personal privacy, as an attack on the whole basis of its existence.

And yet they need one another. Their aerial combat and pursuit in flight are an indispensable part of their life. Alongside bitterly contested fights, one can also observe mock battles that are evidently fought for the joy of flight, the fun of performing skilful manoeuvres and from the sheer enjoyment of life. A hummingbird kept in a solitary state is a miserable shadow of what it could be if it had three or four companions of its own species in the cage. It is really alive only when it can indulge in squabbles.

There is a marked difference in their attitude towards each other during the day and at night. During the day each hummingbird claims an area about eighteen inches in circumference which it defends from competitors, but at night it seeks the proximity of others. It is true that their bodies do not actually touch but they are only an inch or two apart. One can see them sleeping in a row on the outermost branches of a shrub or tree, looking like some rare fruit, perched close alongside each other, their bills raised vertically like thorns as common protection.

When they go for a bath they also fly together. Here, too, there is

151

squabbling and fighting. They all seem to want to go into the water at the same spot even though there are plenty of other places available. They give the impression that they bathe only because another bird has begun to do so.

The same applies to their singing. When they hear the song of another in the distance, the whole lot bursts into song and they keep it up for hours on end. Then something happens which changes the picture completely. One moment they are singing while perching peaceably and then there is a rattling or creaking sound, presumably made by the bird acting as sentry, and the whole lot fly up into the air without any perceptible signal – who knows why? Then a chase starts in which they weave in and out amongst each other, screaming their heads off, beating their wings and apparently yelling for help, as though a murder were being committed. There is a frightful commotion even though there seems to be nothing to justify it. In this way, however, they provide mutual stimulation and keep each other on the alert.

When one bird is being chased too much by another and starts to run out of breath, it cries for help; two or three other birds, even quite small ones, fly to it regardless of any danger to themselves and help ward off the attacker. Some honest citizens could well afford to follow this example of civic responsibility and individual courage from the hummingbird world. The fact that a pursued hummingbird can count on the help of others, so that the aggressor's intentions are deflected, is one of the reasons that it is easier to keep four or more hummingbirds than only two, even if the two happen to be a pair.

Curiosity greater than fear On one occasion when the fighting was too much for me I intervened. While I was cleaning the aviary I watched a Blue-throated Sylph attacking an *Amazilia*, giving it no peace at all. Exasperated, I threw a rag in its direction. Instead of flying away, it made a bold, defensive turn, shot behind the rag and flew around it, its tail feathers spread and so close to the rag that it almost touched it. Immediately other hummingbirds arrived at the spot. A lively dance began around the newly arrived 'bird' which lay on the floor. They did everything they could to provoke it to some kind of response, continually issuing challenges and 'insulting' it by strenuously beating their wings. They flew away only when it became obvious that the 'bird' was really a boring, lifeless object.

When I waved a stick at a Brown Inca that was buzzing round my head and pulling at my hair, it faced the stick in the air and kept watch on it. Everything out of the ordinary, be it large or small, harmless or frightening, arouses their curiosity. Instead of remaining at a safe distance with necks extended, they fly to and fro at the strange object, and literally stick their nose into it. If a nest box is hung up they are there in a flash. If a nail is hammered into the wall and the hammer is left lying about, it causes screams and a humming of wings as the birds report when and where something is not in order. If a strange person appears in front of the glass pane, they immediately fly over to look at him, naturally always ready to fly off but showing hostility at the same time. If one of them is unfortunate enough to get caught somewhere and calls anxiously, the others join it on the spot and express noisy sympathy.

Intelligence tests Their curiosity points to an alert intelligence. They are aware of every change in their environment and react to it. An experiment with a Blue-throated Sylph (*Aglaiocercus kingi*) also showed that they have an astonishing memory.

I kept this bird flying free in my study. It went back into the aviary only to feed. As it was a particularly beautiful specimen, I had decided to exhibit it in a show. One day before the show I stopped it from flying into the aviary to feed and hung a bottle on the wall in the room opposite the aviary. It soon found the bottle and used it throughout the day. That evening I caught the bird and took it to the show where it remained for five days.

After its return I tested its ability to remember. I again hung the feeding-bottle on the wall opposite the aviary but hung a cloth in front of it and left the aviary door closed. Then I carried the travelling cage into my room and released the bird. I expected it to fly first to the aviary window, attracted by the red feeding-bottles of the other birds which were visible behind the glass.

Instead of flying towards the aviary window it immediately turned towards the door; it had clearly not forgotten its normal way of entering the aviary. So far so good. But the door was closed. It flew up and down restlessly in front of the door for two minutes. All of a sudden it turned away and flew straight as a die to the opposite wall, circled around the cloth behind which was the bottle,

153

and reached its objective. An astonishing feat of memory after five days of absence.

Their ability to adapt is equally good. I carried out an experiment with a *Hylocharis leucotis* designed to show how long it took a hummingbird to adjust to a new situation.

I took the bird from the communal aviary and put it into a solitary glass cage. At a certain place I hung up its usual red feeding-bottle. The bird saw it immediately, flew to it and drank from it regularly for three days. On the fourth day I left the red bottle empty, but at the same time hung up a filled blue bottle in another corner of the cage. Hummingbirds are used to flying to one and the same feeding spot with great persistence. Like all the hummingbirds, *Hylocharis* showed a preference for the colour red and it had been accustomed to feeding from a red bottle for more than a year. I was therefore curious to know how long it would take before it

1. recognised the new blue bottle in another position as a feeding place.
2. gave up abortive flights to the empty red bottle.

In dealing with the first problem the bird would have to cope with two difficulties, namely, a change in colour and a change in position of the feeding-bottle. In dealing with the second, its intelligence would be tested as it needed to 'think-around' the new situation, and then adapt correctly to it. The result was interesting:

1145 hrs Red feeding-bottle removed from the cage. Allowed the bird to fast for half an hour.

1215 hrs Red bottle suspended in its old position, *but empty*. A new blue feeding-bottle suspended in a distant corner, *filled*.

1215 to 1220 hrs During these five minutes the bird flew – in vain – twenty-four times to the red bottle.

1221 hrs The bird begins to search.

1222 hrs After a minute's search it discovers the blue bottle, recognises it as a feeding place and drinks from it. (For its next meal the bird will have to pass the red bottle on its way to the blue. Will it attempt to drink there first and if so, how often?)

1225 hrs Flies to the red – in vain – then without further search to the blue; drinks.

1226 hrs Flies to the red – in vain. Then to the blue, drinks.

1228 hrs Flies to the red – in vain. Then to the blue, drinks.

154

1228 to 1234 hrs The bird rests on its branch.

1234 hrs Direct flight to the blue (no attention paid to the red bottle).

1235 hrs Direct flight to the blue.

1236 hrs Direct flight to the blue; from now on, always to the blue.

At first the bird showed perseverance. It flew twenty-four times to the accustomed filling station. The bird's previous conditioning held strong, but it soon learned where to get its food from and after a minute or so of searching it had recognised the new feeding place and accepted it. It allowed itself to be deceived only four times by the familiar red bottle which it had been using for months. What surprised me most was that after a rest of only six minutes, it flew direct to the blue bottle, although the red one was hanging right in front of its nose!

In a total of nine minutes the hummingbird had learnt to reorientate itself correctly to a new position. It is said that the weight of a hummingbird's brain, in proportion to its body weight, is greater than that of most other birds. It would also seem that they know how to make use of this extra mass.

A man for a sleeping perch Although hummingbirds are generally creatures of habit, it can happen that for some obscure reason they suddenly alter their ways. The saying that there is no rule without an exception apparently applies also to hummingbirds. The Blue-throated Sylph, *Aglaiocercus kingi*, that flew free in my room occupied a permanent perch on my desk. For sleeping it flew into a hibiscus plant on the bookshelves. It had never shown any signs in the evening of flying over to join the other members of its species in the aviary. It remained solitary and appeared to be in fine condition. One day my father-in-law came on a visit. He is large and powerfully built, rather like a tree, and he wears horn-rimmed spectacles. He often spent the day with me in the room, where the Blue-throated Sylph flew round him, examined him closely and accepted him. One evening something remarkable took place.

It was time for the hummingbirds to take up their sleeping quarters. Sitting opposite me on the sofa, my father-in-law watched the evening ritual in which the birds flew off one after the other, each to its own perch, followed by the usual squabbling amongst themselves, and finally took up their sleeping positions.

155

After this the Blue-throated Sylph also flew off from its daytime perch, but instead of setting its usual course for the bookcase, it flew straight at my father-in-law and settled down on the side-piece of his spectacles, just as though it had been planning this move all day; it then leant its breast against his temple, raised its little bill, and made it quite clear that it intended to sleep there and nowhere else.

My father-in-law got up and walked around. This did not upset the bird, which remained on its unaccustomed perch. After a while, I took it carefully in my hands and placed it on the hibiscus plant. Immediately it was up and away and after taking a turn round the room it perched once again on the spectacles. Not that my father-in-law had any objection, on the contrary, but how was *he* to get any sleep?

We assumed that the bird was attracted to the spectacles because of the similarity of the sidepieces to bits of twig. My father-in-law removed his spectacles with the bird still on them and put them down gently on the bookcase. But this did not suit the Blue-throated Sylph. It left the cold place and landed again on my father-in-law's head. It snuggled down into his hair and began to sleep.

There was nothing we could do except pick it up and throw it back into the room from the doorway as we quickly left the room. Its language was appropriate, but we shut the door before it could follow us.

More obstinate than an elephant

From the way in which they flutter, whir, dance and shoot about in the air, as light as feathers, one might judge hummingbirds to be fickle and changeable in nature. In fact, it is difficult to beat a hummingbird for strength of character, tenacity and toughness. The migratory species provide an example of tremendous energy and a veritable unshakable determination to achieve their goal. In captivity one can readily observe how much of their daily life is subject to rules and habits. Each individual hummingbird conquers, occupies and dominates a perch. Visitors who have seen a certain hummingbird sitting on a particular branch in my aviary have found it still perching in the same place a year later.

They prefer not to take the first that happens to be available. The greater the selection the more selective they become. I do not know why, but their first choice always seems to be one that is already in another bird's possession. This naturally results in tough fights. The persistence of the aggressor defies description. Again and again it comes in to the attack and tries to dislodge the other. A small branch a little farther away, which in my opinion looks just as desirable, may well be free. But no, it is determined to have the one it wants and no other. Its persistence presupposes an iron will and is exceeded only by the determined stubbornness of the sitting tenant.

It is also remarkable how long and carefully a hummingbird tests out one of the sleeping places which it has put on its short list. It approaches it from all directions, lowers itself on to it, flies out backwards, hurries in from the other side, glides off forwards, comes up again from below and soars away upwards. After half an hour of diligent practice of all the possible ways of landing and taking-off, it may still not be satisfied and begin the same performance all over again somewhere else.

After a few days, however, each one has the equivalent of its seat on which it perches, its table at which it eats and its bed in which it sleeps. The air space is also divided up to some extent. It is disastrous, however, if a branch becomes rotten and breaks off. The hummingbird which had its home there has now lost it, but it cannot and will not believe that this has happened. It may make as many as a hundred attempts to land in the same spot; it continues to hover over it, buzzes around excitedly and searches. It resembles a man whose house has been burnt down and who sees his misfortune but cannot take it in. It may take a long time before the homeless hummingbird is content with a new perch.

Can hummingbirds be tamed? Hummingbirds have always given me the impression that when they see a human, it is as though they were thinking how he could best be used to their own advantage. They fly around one without any sign of alarm and come really close. An electrical fitter who was repairing the wiring inside the aviary was circled by them at such close quarters that he was hardly able to concentrate on his work. He had an unlit cigar in his mouth and a Blue-throated Sylph perched stubbornly on it, the thin shape apparently offering an ideal grip for the hummingbird's claws. He had to keep driving it off like a troublesome wasp.

Even newly arrived birds show this boldness and it is a mystery to me how they come to be so unafraid of humans. Whether they have

157

become accustomed to man in their country of origin or whether they have not yet come to regard humans as dangerous and unpredictable, I do not know, but they appear to be quite without fear.

Only a few species, such as *Chlorostilbon mellisugus*, *Calothorax lucifer* or *Selasphorus rufus*, are always wary and keep their distance at first. They do indeed fly away when one approaches them, but they never rush off in a panic. After a few days of acclimatisation these species also become so tame that they will drink out of one's hand. Whether they are kept singly or in a community has no influence on the degree of trust they exhibit. This behaviour differentiates them from budgerigars and songbirds which become particularly tame in captivity when they are kept on their own and treated as a companion by a human. The absence of shyness in hummingbirds is not only linked with food but is rooted, in my opinion, in a kind of strongly marked self-reliance; they have confidence in their own speed, power and skill. In this they resemble the elephants.

At home everywhere I have never yet seen a sad hummingbird, unless it was sick. I have never seen any sign that captive hummingbirds miss their freedom. They do not fly to the window or look elsewhere for an exit. Providing they are moderately well cared for, have sufficient room to fly, and enough to drink, nothing appears to damp their spirits.

I therefore regard hummingbirds as ideal cage birds. An experienced aviculturist can keep them without being troubled by the thought that he may be going against the laws of nature. When one has to keep in captivity animals which have a strong urge for freedom, a need to wander about or a fear of humans that cannot be allayed, one's conscience is apt to be troubled. With their known powers of adaptability, their acclimatisation to captivity is only a matter of hours.

Beatles among the songbirds At first I could not help being somewhat critical of the singing ability of hummingbirds but I must now take this back and express my apologies to them. I have gradually acquired an ear for their type of music, just as one learns in the course of time to appreciate Beethoven's Ninth Symphony, Hindemith or Louis Armstrong.

It is true that I could not place them among the opera singers of

158

the bird world, such as the blackbirds, thrushes and nightingales, nor with the operetta stars, the siskins, finches and larks. In my opinion the song of hummingbirds belongs to an even lighter form of music, to the beat world. One could even describe them as the Beatles of the bird world. They twitter, squawk and twang; at least they sound cheerful even if they do not give us any particular aesthetic pleasure.

There are even a few species, whose song sounds just as pleasant as that of a warbler or a starling, even if it is not as loud and does not carry as far. *Hylocharis leucotis* has an attractive phrase which it sings the whole day long almost without a break; it sounds like the ringing of a silver bell, a pleasant and unobtrusive little song.

Colibri coruscans is also an ardent performer. Its recital is somewhat monotonous and difficult to describe but it is quite attractive. *Amazilia tzacatl* makes music year in year out with hardly a break. In addition to clear twittering notes it also produces a gurgle, a squawk and a twang which at a distance resemble the song of a European starling.

I have been astonished at the tonal range of this little singer, which extends from deep guttural sounds up to the highest trills. In addition to their song they have a wide variety of lively sounds at their disposal which one soon learns to interpret. *Amazilia tzacatl* gives a short, raucous cry when it flies over to feed, meaning 'look out, here I come.' It also has a war cry. When it rushes at an opponent it gives a long trill. In my community of fifty or sometimes up to a hundred hummingbirds, this *Amazilia* took over the role of sentry. When danger threatened it chattered like a magpie, calling rapidly 'chak–chak–chak' while making short dashes to and fro in the air.

The Blue-tailed Emerald, *Chlorostilbon mellisugus*, uttered a very high twitter, sometimes a hissing sound. During its strenuous display flights this dwarf increased the tempo of its song, repeating the phrases to the point of breathlessness. The Long-billed Starthroat, *Heliomaster longirostris*, croaked like a frog, making for a most comical effect.

They sometimes sing without opening the bill. Some research workers are of the opinion that they can produce notes of a higher frequency than the human ear is able to detect. I have carried out observations in this area and of the thirty different species of

159

hummingbird in this book, I have never seen one whose throat feathers vibrated in the way that is characteristic of singing, without at the same time hearing some kind of sound. The Sword-billed Hummingbird, *Ensifera ensifera*, never uttered a sound of any kind all the time that I had it. It was as silent as the grave.

Always active　During the first weeks after I had received my hummingbirds, if anyone had asked me when they spent most time flying, I would have replied: 'They are almost *always* flying.' Intense activity was continuous in the aviary and every individual was always in the air.

Later I realised that like all living organisms they have periods of great activity and periods of comparative rest. In the morning, during the first two or three hours after daylight, there is a humming sound as though a swarm of bees were setting out on a journey. At this time they vibrate and drink and chase each other more than that at any other time of day. Breakfast consists of dozens of snacks and there are the usual early morning brawls and chases; after this there is a short pause while they rest for a while, flying over to the feeding-bottles only now and again, and digest their food.

It is not long before the second round of activity gets under way. There is a general flurry as they bathe and preen their plumage. They take a long time over their bathing and they clean themselves carefully.

It is not until about midday that something akin to peace descends on the community for several hours. One can still see stray individuals flying fairly regularly to the feeding-bottles. During the afternoon there is more movement, and towards evening this increases to a second climax. Thus the periods of greatest activity are in the morning and shortly before dusk. It is for this reason, as I have already mentioned, that I am convinced that it is wrong to give them only honey at these times. I believe that it is particularly important to give them a substantial meal, containing all the nutrients, at the time they need it most. With their fast metabolism, everything is digested in twenty minutes at the most, and no worthwhile reserve remains in the stomach and intestines overnight. When the hummingbirds awake in the morning, they are particularly hungry and behave accordingly.

How to photograph hummingbirds in flight

First attempts

An Egyptologist
in the rain-forest

How should one set about photographing hummingbirds? According to Dr Hesse, who is an amateur photographer as well as a chemist and an Egyptologist, one merely has to go to wherever the hummingbirds are and stalk them with a camera and electronic flash. Having delivered himself of this statement one day, he stepped straight into my tropical aviary and bravely set off into the wilds of the rain-forest. The atmosphere of my luxuriant winter garden was warm and damp and living free amongst the tropical vegetation were about a hundred hummingbirds, from almost all the countries of North, South and Central America.

The good doctor who specialised in photographing Pharaohs at rest found that a hummingbird in flight presented quite a different set of problems. A tiny, unpredictable bird that is as fast as a dragonfly is not an object which can be posed, illuminated and photographed, nor is it willing to wait patiently like a model in a studio, at the correct distance from the camera for the convenience of the photographer.

The *Amazilia* species, the Sylphs and the Nymphs, accompanied by swarms of fruitflies all buzzed and hummed around him. He scarcely knew where to look or where to set up his camera. While he was suffering from the heat of an electric lamp directed at his bald head, all the birds seemed to be thoroughly enjoying the situation, watching his careful movements and elaborate preparations. They whirred in front of his nose just as he was about to point the camera at a promising subject. When he was defenceless with both hands engaged with his apparatus, busy focussing on a bird, they landed on his head. They sat on his equipment, covering both light and lens with their tail-feathers. When they were chased away they returned immediately. After all, it was the first time that they had met a distinguished scholar at such close quarters, not to mention his photographic apparatus which they found particularly exciting. They would not have been hummingbirds if they had not thought all this worthy of their attention, and by way of demonstrating their sense of occasion, they celebrated in typical fashion, whirring and twittering energetically all the time. Soon the enthusiastic hummingbird hunter became the hunted, and within a few hours the energetic investigator had become a nervy man urgently in need of a rest. The sweat poured down his face as he stood on a ladder and became entangled in the coils of a *Tatra stegma*. At this point I began to worry quite genuinely about his welfare and I asked him how he was feeling.

'Fine! The job is beginning to amuse me,' he replied in an agonised tone without taking his eyes off the hummingbirds. But I had the impression that the amusement was all on the side of the hummingbirds.

He took one photograph after another as though possessed. He was determined to get the birds in flight and he certainly did not spare the film. But when the results were developed most of the exposures were blank. In the first batch there were a few showing tails and wing tips, a mass of leaves, lamps and parts of the aviary, but there was not a single picture showing the whole hummingbird and still less one revealing the typical iridescence. It was the sparkling jewel-like quality of these birds which had first attracted him, as he felt himself to be something of a specialist in this, having had the experience of photographing the scintillating gold and jewels of Pharaohs and ancient Egyptian graves.

Hummingbirds are not ducks The photographs which happened to show the wings lacked sharpness, which was a pity, as they would have been useful for seeing how the feathers were positioned. After some weeks of fruitless exertion and some hundreds of exposures, we had to admit that hummingbirds could not be hunted as one hunts hares, ducks or pheasants. After all, a camera is not like a shotgun, which can be simply triggered off at an object such as a hare that gives the hunter time to take aim.

We wanted to get pictures of hummingbirds in all their beauty and elegance, with wings and tail spread, the bill and eye clearly visible, and the iridescence of their plumage showing to advantage. To achieve this it was necessary to have a specially designed fast shutter release with an exposure of only a fraction of a second at a set distance.

Neither the costly miniature camera nor the flash, timed to 1/200 or 1/600 of a second, proved adequate. With the small field of vision, it happened all too often that the bird flew out of the frame. Details of the pattern were lost. The duration of the electronic flash was too long. It is true that in bird photography one puts up with slightly unsharp images made by wing movements, in order to give the subject a more natural appearance, but even at 1/600 of a second the wings of the hummingbird no longer looked like the wings of a bird but like a transparent feather-duster that bore no relation to the sharply delineated bird. This is not surprising since the wings beat about fifty times per second, and the wing tips cover a distance of about forty-five feet in that time. Somewhat resentful, the good doctor retired to the pyramids and I was forced to find other ways of carrying on the photography.

The technical equipment

Camera   I found just the precision instrument in a Linhof Technika, a large format camera for professional photographers with a Super-Rollex cassette 9 by 12. The large format gave me considerably more scope in regard to the height and breadth of the picture frame. Providing I worked within certain limits, I was able to capture, with some likelihood of success, even a very fast moving object without having to be farther than twenty-eight inches away. Also, better use could be made of the larger negative than when working with miniature film.

I used a Rodenstock Apo-Ronar lens, focal length 150 mm, with a Synchro-Compur shutter 0. This camera proved to be a great step forwards, but only the first step.

Human reaction is too slow to keep up with a bird shooting past the camera only an arm's length away. It was therefore necessary for the shutter to be released electromagnetically, with the film being wound on automatically as the bird flew through a light trap – interrupting a beam of light. Thus the Technika had to undergo some changes. It received a special front plate with a magnetic release mechanism and a minute precision electric motor which reset the shutter.

The crucial and most difficult problem of all was the speed of the bird and the time lag of the camera release. The bird had to be caught by the electronic flash at the moment it flew through the light trap and the shutter had to open at the same time. This process had to be completed in not more than eight-thousandths of a second if the bird was to be kept in the frame and in the plane of focus.

This problem was solved by Edgar Mönch of Munich, an engineer and designer of special photographic apparatus. The relays, which were activated by the light trap, used about six volts with a resistance of ninety ohms. Mönch shortened the contact distance by pinching the shutter leaves with pliers close to the point of contact so that the magnet would operate with a minimum of mechanical work. This relay closed the circuit of a 75 volt anode

166

The author with his photographic equipment – camera, switch gear and lighting cabinet.

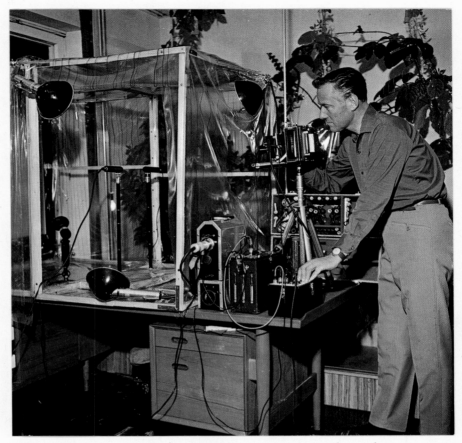

battery, which supplied electrical current to the release magnet. Mönch did not allow the release pin to act on the lever of the camera shutter, as in other solenoid shutters, but directly on the closure of the tension ring, which he achieved by boring through its casing. An adjustable screw pressed the release pin almost completely down. The release mechanism was adjusted so finely that the shutter blades operated only one five-hundredth of a second after the light trap was set off, and the exposure took place after a two-hundredth of a second. By this means the contact had to travel only about one-tenth of a millimetre.

Mönch not only shortened the release path, but eliminated all time-wasting levers. He increased the reaction speed of the camera so decisively that the electromagnetic delay between the bird interrupting the light beam and the exposure being taken was only six-thousandths of a second, that is, about three milliseconds for the magnet and three milliseconds for the shutter.

This push-button operation gave excellent results. Even the fastest hummingbird, once caught by the magic eye, appeared in the picture. What the picture looked like was quite another matter.

Electronic flash In one second the wing tips of a flying hummingbird are able to cover a distance of about forty-five feet. When photographed with an electronic flash lasting one five-hundredth of a second, a whole phase of movement was recorded in the picture; the wings have moved a distance of three-quarters of an inch; the result was an unacceptable, blurred image.

I therefore used a Mannesmann electronic flash with normal amplifier and three lamps with a flash duration of only about one five-thousandth of a second. Even with this, in unfavourable circumstances, a small loss of focus (up to $\frac{1}{16}$ inch) was still apparent, but these results were not optically disturbing and in fact yielded an exact representation of the feathers even to the eye of a trained ornithologist.

The bird was illuminated by two flashes from in front, the third being placed at the side to the rear so that in addition to the iridescence, I also captured a three-dimensional effect with points of light on head, bill and wing feathers.

Light trap A light trap consists of two small metal containers, each about the size and shape of a cigar. One holds a light beam produced by a tungsten lamp (6 volts, $\frac{1}{2}$ ampere) and the other a receiver. Both can be positioned opposite each other vertically, horizontally, obliquely or as one wishes.

The beam of light is about as thick as a man's finger, and when it is interrupted the transistors come into operation, releasing the relay which closes a circuit and activates the electronic flash and camera.

The light from the lamp is directed into a parallel beam by means of a lens, and it acts like a small searchlight. The lamp is positioned in such a way that its beam strikes the receiver where it illuminates a germanium photo-cell.

The functioning of this switch is astonishingly precise, sensitive and fast. It will even react when one passes a pencil as fast as one can through the light ray. The pencil will be photographed at the exact moment that it interrupts the ray. The same thing happens when a

168

bird flies through it.

The principal item of the equipment was the switching installation with its condensors, relay and switches. Enclosed in a close-fitting plastic container, the electrical leads formed a criss-cross network throughout the unit. From here the electronic flash, camera release, shutter and film-winding could be operated automatically or even by hand. The birds alone determined the operation. What was right for one miscarried with another. The relay and motor were powered by a 75 volt anode battery. I used Kodak Ektachrome 19 Din film. My photographic studio was a kind of large cage with walls of transparent plastic sheeting on which the bird could not hurt or damage itself. Every movement of the hummingbird could be seen from outside and possibly influenced. The camera stood outside. An opening in the sheeting acted as a peephole for the lens and, incidentally, provided an escape route for the bird to get into the workroom which it used all too often.

Tripods for flowers and branches and for the other items that are part of the working gear of every professional photographer completed the equipment. The following accessories also proved to be indispensable:

a mirror, a feather duster, a hand-broom, a rubber balloon, an old man's hat, paper streamers, tennis balls, a gaily coloured kitchen apron and a mouse on wheels.

These objects served to provide amusement for the hummingbird, to encourage it to focus its attention on something briefly and to vary its 'facial expression' according to the requirements of the photographer. Sometimes it worked, but usually the opposite of what was expected took place.

Methods

*By accident
or design*   Even with such marvellous equipment – including the hat and
balloon – I often came closer to despair than to success. One
technique can be combined with another. Providing one has
thought out his theory well and done all the calculations properly,
then it should all work out in practice. Even humans will sometimes
allow themselves to be classified and treated like machines in spite of
the fact that it may not be entirely to their liking. But this does not
work with an animal, least of all with a hummingbird.

It was practically impossible to photograph the hummingbirds in
their communal aviary. They whirred in and out amongst each
other far too much. As soon as one was in focus, another shot in
between and spoilt the picture. In addition, the working conditions
were unsatisfactory; there was too much variation in range and the
nature of the background in the aviary made it unsuitable.

Each bird had, therefore, to be caught up singly – a job in itself –
and photographed alone in the photographic enclosure. Naturally I
wanted to photograph only healthy birds with perfect plumage that
were in good condition and strong on the wing, but no hummingbird was ever delivered to me in this condition. New arrivals always
had dirty plumage that was damaged in some way, often with
feathers missing, and so I had first to keep them for some months,
sometimes until after the next moult, before I could photograph
them. And when the great day came, it happened on more than one
occasion that while the bird was being caught or at the moment of
release, it lost all of its handsome tail-feathers. All my trouble had
been in vain.

The photographic enclosure had to be large enough for the effect
of light and shadow to operate, but not too large, otherwise the bird
had too extensive an area in which to fly, and this reduced the
chances of its flying through the light trap. Finding the correct
mean took a lot of time and a lot of experimenting.

The light trap was so arranged that the path of its beam cut
approximately through the centre of the enclosure. In the vicinity

170

but still outside the picture area a perch and feeding-bottle were installed. Hence the bird should have to fly through the light trap on one of its flights, thus interrupting the ray and thereby automatically releasing the shutter and the electronic flash.

At first I overestimated the chances of the bird touching this imaginary line that floated in the air and was about eight inches long. As it turned out I had to wait a long time. On the average one hundred and fifty flights to and fro had to take place before the light trap was even operated. Admittedly, the bird was then photographed but not necessarily in a satisfactory manner. The position of the wings, head, body or bill could still look disappointing in the result. There was only one in a hundred exposures that satisfied all the requirements. The bird had therefore to perform on average about fifteen thousand flights to and fro before I got a perfect picture. This procedure could well take a week. Later I studied the line of flight taken habitually, over a period of time, by each hummingbird as it took off and landed. These studies revealed individual differences. For example, one bird would fly off more or less horizontally and land by approaching the branch from below. There were many variants which were discovered only after the bird had been allowed to get used to the conditions in the photographic enclosure and had developed a certain flight rhythm.

I prepared a series of flight sketches for each bird, from which I adjusted the position of the perch according to individual requirements, thus increasing the chances of the bird flying through the beam of the light trap. In this way, I was able to reduce the number of flights to about half. But it still needed about 80 for each exposure and eight thousand to obtain the perfect picture.

In spite of all my stratagems and calculations, it took even longer to photograph certain hummingbirds, as they displayed diabolical cunning and repeatedly shot over or under the place where the beam of light was directed. On these occasions their intelligence and adaptability set me some serious problems.

Management combined with endless patience How does one make a hummingbird fly in front of the camera in the photographic enclosure? At first they are stubborn and refuse to perform. They want to get out of the enclosure, because they can hear their companions twittering somewhere outside. They fly high up above or to one side, anywhere except where one wants them to go and it may take hours before they land for the first time on the branch near the camera. Some avoid the light beam from the start because they distrust the thing, others after the first flash. Some perch on the apparatus and activate the release mechanism with their tail.

Everything does not work out automatically and according to plan. The birds need managing and one has to distract their attention from the light trap by every conceivable means. The things which one uses to arouse their interest cannot be too curious. (See under 'Important accessories'.) It is also necessary to provide variety because they soon become bored by even the most remarkable objects. One can take down the light trap, hang up a feeding-bottle in its place, allow the bird to fly to it twenty or thirty times, then remove the bottle and re-install the light trap – and it flies into the trap. The same thing happens when one wants to make the bird come to a flower. For months it has been accustomed to a feeding-bottle, and it also expects to find one in the photographic enclosure. If you provide it with one, it is perfectly happy and it will not make any attempt to visit a flower, even if it is the finest bloom fresh from the garden and of a variety normally loved by hummingbirds. Only a long period of acclimatisation to the change will help in such cases.

Although it is difficult to get them in front of the camera, it is easy to get them on it. They have a remarkable attachment to the black box, which they try to reach through a hole. There is nothing one can do except to be on the alert all the time, ready to chase them away immediately before they escape into the room. The hand-broom or feather duster are useful for this purpose. Every hummingbird has to be outwitted in its own way. One needs a gift for observation and a capacity to sense what is happening. The only other quality which is recommended is patience – the patience of Job.

A hundred exposures for one good photograph

The standard required for good animal photographs today is very high. The photographs may serve several purposes. To a zoologist, for instance, the picture must be sufficiently clear for him to identify the species. The ornithologist wants to see the form and colour clearly and the details of the head, bill, eyes, wings and tail; often he can recognise the exact species or subspecies only from tiny details. I have tried to fulfil this requirement in my photographs.

172

To the aviculturist all this may not be so important. What appeals to him is the charm of the particular bird as it preens itself or sits on its eggs. I have tried to capture something of this also.

The naturalist wants an impression of the whole way of life of the bird, all on one picture, and this too I have tried to reproduce.

The artist likes a beautiful composition, with form and line, light and space cleverly balanced, and colours that are either restrained or flamboyant or entirely in black-and-white. I hope that I have had some success in this field too.

Printers and publishers demand clean work, good technique, reliable materials and something that will not be too expensive to reproduce. To meet their requirements has not been a simple matter. Scarcely a single picture is the result of pure chance. I spent a lot of time just watching the birds before deciding in what position I wanted to photograph them. I watched them both in flight and when perching, from various angles and in various lights, trying to catch them when their plumage showed to best advantage, even if it was only for a fraction of a second as they landed, took off or spread their tail-feathers. I wanted to record them at the precise moment in which they looked their best.

Each species presented fresh problems. Sometimes it was the special way in which they approached a flower that interested me, sometimes it was the relationship between one hummingbird and another that caught my eye. If I saw something on one occasion, I knew that it must happen again at some other time. It was this moment that I waited for, a brief flash in a scene that was constantly changing with incredible rapidity. It is not surprising that it took me weeks to achieve certain pictures and then only after a great many false attempts.

It was necessary to ask a great deal of my hummingbirds, not anything, however, that was beyond their powers. I have to admit that on more than one occasion they almost defeated me.

It was not only the live birds that played tricks on me. The mechanics of photography also tripped me up. I took twenty films, all with beautiful shots on them – or so I thought – but each picture was as dark and dismal as the night. The work of one whole period of leave was wasted because one contact, a tiny screw which nobody regarded as important, had shifted its position. And my feelings were as gloomy as the pictures that emerged.

173

Having sorted and rejected the headless, tailless and wingless hummingbirds, and the shots showing the birds in bad positions or where the colour rendering was unsatisfactory, I was left with a ratio of about 10000 : 100. In other words I had found it necessary to take about one hundred exposures in order to get one good result. But the joy over the one good picture was worth all the trouble.

In praise of the creation

'The grace of their form, the beauty of their colours, the speed and agility of their movements, the music of their voices, the charm of their very essence attract us irresistibly.

'The first men of whom we have any knowledge made friends with the birds; the savages took them under their protection; poets of yore and of the present have been inspired by them. Their liveliness, their voices, their flight, their visible enjoyment of life elevate and refresh us.'

Thus wrote Alfred Edmund Brehm. He was writing about birds in general but his words are particularly applicable to hummingbirds. Years of work with hummingbirds, and for them, have left me with no regrets. Their beauty, their lively activity, 'their visible enjoyment of life', have given me endless pleasure. What more could I have said about them in this book?

Even if I had compiled all the published reports, observations and research on them together with my own few contributions, the problems surrounding them would still be far from solved.

Even if I had been able to describe the charm of their appearance in the words of a poet and to illustrate them with perfect pictures, I would still not have succeeded. No words or pictures can do justice to these creatures which are a miracle of beauty, vitality and colourful splendour.

Index

Abeillia abeillei, 23
Acestrura mulsanti, 18, 23, 31, 32, 61
Aglaeactis cupripennis, 24
Aglaiocercus kingi, 23, 31, 53, 61, 67, 79, 103, 112, 118, 148, 153, 155
Amazilia franciae, 31, 47, 61, 102
Amazilia iodura, 31, 118
Amazilia tzacatl, 23, 31, 47, 49, 56, 61, 78, 102, 118, 148, 159
Anatomy, 31–34
Anthracothorax nigricollis, 31, 56
Archilochus colubris, 21–23, 53, 55, 63, 103
Arphantocroa, 23
Augastes lumachellus, 22, 95, 96

Bathing, 117, 118
Behaviour, 149–60
Bills, 32
Boissonneaua flavescens, 31
Boissonneaua jardini, 18, 23, 31, 61, 68, 103
Breeding, 72–85

Cages, see Captivity
Calliphlox amethystina, 23, 61
Calothorax lucifer, 23, 31, 32, 38, 39, 55, 61, 62, 158
Calypte anna, 23
Calypte costae, 23
Calypte helenae, 103
Camera, 166, 167
Campylopterus, 23
Captivity, 94, 95, 97, 104–20, 158
Capture methods, 24–30
Catching flies, 47, 48
Chalcostigma herrani, 24
Chlorestes notatus, 61
Chlorostilbon aureoventris, 23
Chlorostilbon mellisugus, 31, 56, 80, 102, 118, 158, 159
Chrysolampis mosquitus, 23, 31, 47, 49, 56, 61, 78, 103, 148

Cinnyris venustus falkensteini, 54
Clytolaema rubricauda, 23
Coeligena torquata, 31
Coeligena wilsoni, 18, 24, 31, 55, 61, 79–81, 84, 143, 148, 150
Colibri coruscans, 9, 24, 31, 61, 81, 97, 102, 118, 159
Colibri cyanotus, 31, 40, 56, 118
Colibri delphinae greenewalti, 22, 96
Colibri thalassimus, 52
Colour, see Plumage
Coquette, Frilled, 37, 101
Coronet, Velvet-purple, 68, 103
Courtship, 48, 79–81

Damophila julie, 31, 61, 78, 84, 102, 118, 148
Distribution, 20–24

Egg sizes, 84
Egg-laying, 81–3
Electronic flash, 168
Emerald, Blue-tailed, 80, 102, 159
Endurance, 62–4
Ensifera ensifera, 30, 31, 61, 67, 118, 160
Eugenes fulgens, 24
Eulampis jugularis, 24
Eupetomena macruora, 61
Eutoxeres aquila, 31, 56
Ezra, Alfred, 120

Feathers, see Plumage
Feeding, 65–8, 119–48
Fighting, 149–52
Flight, 38–64
Florisuga mellivora, 56
Food, see Feeding

Greenewalt, C. H., 14, 94, 120

Heart beat, 32
Heliaction cornuta, 23

Heliangelus clarissae, 24
Heliodoxa rubinoides, 31, 56, 80, 118
Heliomaster constantii, 23
Heliomaster furcifer, 23
Heliomaster longirostris, 31, 56, 118, 159
Heliothryx aurita, 23
Heliothryx barroti, 23, 61
Hummingbird, Bee, 30, 39
    Blue-throated, 36
    Calliope, 21
    Giant, 30
    Ruby-throated, 21, 36, 52, 53, 63, 67, 70, 71, 103
    Ruby-topaz, 103
    Rufous, 21, 63, 103
    Sword-billed, 30, 61, 66, 67, 85, 100, 103, 118, 160
Hylocharis leucotis, 31, 48, 56, 61, 84, 102, 127–36, 154, 159
Hylocharis sapphirina, 23
Hylocharis xantusi, 23

Inca, Brown, 55, 72, 77, 79, 84, 136, 143, 144, 150, 153
Incubation, 83–5
Insects as food, see Feeding
Intelligence tests, 153–5
Iridescence, see Plumage

Klais, 24

Lampornis clemenciae, 79, 81
Lamprolaima rhami, 24
Lesbia victoriae, 24, 30, 31, 61, 102, 118
Leucochloris, 23
Light trap, 168, 169
Loddigesia mirabilis, 24
Lophornis magnifica, 23, 37, 101

Melanotrochilus, 23, 61
Mellisuga helenae, 30

Mellisuga minima, 84
Migration, 21–2, 63, 64
Mönch, Edgar, 166–7
Myrmia micrura, 23

Nectar, see Feeding
Nestlings, 85
Nests, 72–9
Nomenclature, 17–19

Ocreatus underwoodi, 24
Oreonympha, 24
Oreotrochilus estellae, 24
Orthorhynchus cristatus, 24
Oxypogon, 24

Panterpe insignis, 24
Patagona gigas, 24, 30, 61
Phaethornis eurynome, 23
Phaethornis jopi, 31
Phaethornis longuemareus, 18
Phaethornis ruber, 61
Phaethornis yaruqui, 23

Photography, 163–74
Plants visited, 67, 68
Plumage, 35–7
Popelairia conversii, 30, 31, 61

Ramphodon, 23
Rhodopis vesper, 23
Ruschi, Augusto, 24, 94–6, 101

Sappho sparganura, 23
Selasphorus flammula, 21, 24
Selasphorus platycercus, 24, 46
Selasphorus rufus, 21, 24, 31, 55, 56, 63, 84, 103, 158
Selasphorus torridus, 24
Sephanoides sephanoides, 24
Singing, 152, 158–60
Size, 30, 31
Sleep, 68–70
Speed of flight, 52, 53, 54
Starthroat, Long-billed, 159
Stellula calliope, 21
Sunbird, African Variable, 54

Sylph, Blue-throated, 36, 40, 53, 54, 67, 79, 103, 112, 152, 153, 155, 156, 157

Tameness, 157, 158
Temperature requirements, 112–14
Thalurania furcata, 23
Thalurania watertoni, 61
Topaz, Crimson, 101
Topaza pella, 23, 102
Torpidity, 69–71
Trainbearer, Black-throated, 30
Transport, 98–100
Trochilidae, 17

Violet-ear, Sparkling, 9, 81, 97, 102

Weights, 31
Wing-beat frequency, 55–62
Wing structure, 34

Zoological Gardens, Regent's Park, 9